PREFACE

G000142008

Structured questions are only one of the
They are being used increasingly by the G
and 'A' levels. The aim of this book is to
level with additional sources of questions so that they can be used for class tests, revision work, or homework.

In essence the structured question is composed of two parts:

(a) the presentation of material (this can be compared to the stem in an objective item), which may take the form of a graph, table, diagram, passage, etc.; and

(b) a series of short questions built around the material. The questions often become progressively more difficult through the series, although this is not a prerequisite. Each question in the series does not depend to a large extent on previous questions. Structured questions are intended to reflect the teaching situation: the teacher poses a problem and guides the pupils to the answer by using a series of shorter problems.

In an attempt to destroy the semi-myth that exists that various mental abilities can be tested using only objective items, a classification has been introduced after every question, based largely on the taxonomy of Bloom and others, but the higher processes have been condensed. Often different contexts require different abilities and often different teachers assess mental ability in different ways. The classification of questions given is in no way final, and should not be regarded as such. If teachers disagree, then they may wish to change the abilities given, and this is perfectly acceptable, or even desirable.

The following taxonomy has been used, together with the approximate weighting of marks for questions.

Ability	Weighting (per cent)
Knowledge (K)	16
Comprehension (C)	42
Higher processes (H)	42

It has also been thought desirable to include a tentative marking scheme. It is felt that pupils should know more about mark allocations; often, if they do, then they place the emphasis where the emphasis should be. Again it is hoped that the marking schemes given are not restrictive and can, of course, be altered where necessary.

A number of 'A' level pupils have tried these questions, and as a result it has been possible to classify the question difficulty into two general categories: (a) easy to medium; and (b) harder (indicated by an asterisk *).

We believe that the foundation for a sound sixth form chemistry course lies in the area of physical chemistry; hence these questions appear first. The general area for each question is indicated in the title, but no apologies are made for including other areas in any one question. Where appropriate, the latest SI and ASE recommendations have been followed.

The authors would like to acknowledge the help of the following: sixth formers of Wilson's School and Alleyn's School, who have tried out the questions; Mr H N Cleeve, formerly of Kelsey Park School for Boys, Beckenham, who kindly read and commented on the manuscript. Finally thanks to Clare Swain for her patience in the burden of having to type an often indecipherable manuscript.

Julian R L Swain
John S Clarke

1 The mole concept: stoichiometry

1,3-dihydroxybenzene, $C_6H_4(OH)_2$, reacts with iodine solution to give a substituted iodo-derivative. From the following information it is possible to determine the number of moles of iodine which react with one mole of 1,3-dihydroxybenzene.

Relative atomic masses: H = 1, C = 12, O = 16, Na = 23, S = 32

$$I_2 \text{ (aq)} + 2S_2O_3{}^{2-}\text{(aq)} \rightarrow S_4O_6{}^{2-}\text{(aq)} + 2I^-\text{ (aq)}$$

(a) To determine the exact concentration of the iodine solution, $25\ cm^3$ of the iodine solution were titrated with a solution of sodium thiosulphate(VI), $Na_2S_2O_3 \cdot 5H_2O$, containing $24 \cdot 8\ g\,dm^{-3}$.

   (i) What is the relative molecular mass of sodium thiosulphate(VI)-5-water?
   C (1)

   (ii) What is the concentration (in $mol\,dm^{-3}$) of the sodium thiosulphate(VI) solution?
   C (1)

   (iii) It was found that $40 \cdot 0\ cm^3$ of the sodium thiosulphate(VI) were required for the end point using starch as indicator. What is the concentration (in $mol\,dm^{-3}$) of the iodine solution?
   C (2)

   (iv) How many moles of iodine would be contained in $50 \cdot 0\ cm^3$ of solution?
   C (1)

(b) (i) The solution of 1,3-dihydroxybenzene contains $2 \cdot 2\ g\,dm^{-3}$. What is the concentration (in $mol\,dm^{-3}$)?
   C (2)

   (ii) How many moles of 1,3-dihydroxybenzene would be contained in $25 \cdot 0\ cm^3$ of this solution?
   C (1)

(c) When $50 \cdot 0\ cm^3$ of the iodine solution were allowed to react with $25 \cdot 0\ cm^3$ of the 1,3-dihydroxybenzene solution in the presence of a buffer solution (a solution to maintain the pH at a fixed value), it was found that the resulting solution required $50 \cdot 0\ cm^3$ of sodium thiosulphate(VI) solution to reach the end point.

   (i) How many moles of iodine remained after the reaction of iodine with 1,3-dihydroxybenzene?
   C (2)

   (ii) How many moles of iodine were used in the reaction?
   C (1)

   (iii) How many moles of iodine would react with one mole of 1,3-dihydroxybenzene?
   C (1)

   (iv) What is the equation for the reaction?
   C (1)

   (v) Suggest a possible structure for the iodo-derivative of 1,3-dihydroxybenzene.
   H (2)

Total   15 marks

2 The mole concept: adsorption†

Adsorption from a solution of organic acids onto activated charcoal usually follows the principles laid down for the adsorption of gases. The degree of adsorption of a solute can be determined by comparing the concentration in a known volume of solution before and after in the form:

$$y = \frac{V(c_0 - c)}{1000\,m}$$

where y is the number of moles of substance adsorbed per gram of adsorbent, $V\,dm^3$ is the volume of the solution, m the mass of the adsorbent in grams, and c_0 and c the initial and equilibrium concentration (in $mol\,dm^{-3}$).

(a) In order to determine the initial concentration of dibasic ethanedioic (oxalic) acid, it was titrated with sodium hydroxide. It was found that, when $20 \cdot 0\,cm^3$ of the acid were titrated with sodium hydroxide (concentration $1 \cdot 25\,mol\,dm^{-3}$) using phenolphthalein as the indicator, $32 \cdot 0\,cm^3$ were required.

    (i) Calculate the number of millimoles of sodium hydroxide in $32 \cdot 0\,cm^3$ of solution.   C(1)

    (ii) Calculate the concentration (in $mol\,dm^{-3}$) of the ethanedioic acid.   C(2)

    (iii) If $40 \cdot 0\,cm^3$ of the acid were added to $60 \cdot 0\,cm^3$ of water, what would be the concentration (in $mol\,dm^{-3}$) of the diluted acid?   C(1)

(b) $100\,cm^3$ of the acid solution in (a)(iii) were shaken with $2 \cdot 00\,g$ of activated charcoal for 30 minutes and allowed to come to equilibrium. The solution was then filtered and $20 \cdot 0\,cm^3$ of the resulting filtrate were titrated with the same sodium hydroxide (concentration $1 \cdot 25\,mol\,dm^{-3}$); $11 \cdot 2\,cm^3$ were required.

    (i) What is the equilibrium concentration (in $mol\,dm^{-3}$) of the ethanedioic acid?   C(2)

    (ii) What is the loss in concentration (in $mol\,dm^{-3}$) due to adsorption?   C(1)

    (iii) What is the number of moles of ethanedioic acid adsorbed per unit mass of charcoal?   H(2)

(c) In order to confirm the equilibrium concentration, $20 \cdot 0\,cm^3$ of the filtrate from (b) were added to $20 \cdot 0\,cm^3$ of sulphuric(VI) acid (concentration $2 \cdot 0\,mol\,dm^{-3}$) and the resulting solution heated to $80\,°C$ and then titrated with potassium manganate(VII) (permanganate).

---

† Adapted from 'Intermolecular Forces: A Project', *S.S.R.*, 1971, **182**, 531.

The redox equations for the reaction are as follows:

$$(COOH)_2 \text{ (aq)} \rightarrow 2CO_2 \text{ (aq)} + 2H^+\text{(aq)} + 2e^-$$

$$MnO_4^-\text{(aq)} + 8H^+\text{(aq)} + 5e^- \rightarrow Mn^{2+}\text{ (aq)} + 4H_2O\text{(l)}$$

(i) How could the concentration of the potassium manganate(VII) be determined accurately?   K (2)

(ii) What is the mole ratio of the ethanedioic acid reacting with the potassium manganate(VII)?   H (2)

(iii) If the concentration of the potassium manganate(VII) is 0·20 mol dm^{-3} and 14·0 cm^3 were required to react with the acid, calculate the equilibrium concentration (in mol dm^{-3}) of the ethanedioic acid.   C (2)

Total   15 marks

3 The determination of the Avogadro constant

The following question is concerned with the determination of the Avogadro constant L by two separate methods. You will require the following information:

Relative atomic mass of copper $= 63\cdot5$

Charge on an electron $= 1\cdot60 \times 10^{-19}$ coulombs

Molar volume of any gas at s.t.p. $= 22\cdot4\,dm^3$

(a) In a certain electrolysis experiment using copper(II) sulphate(VI) solution as electrolyte, $0\cdot213\,g$ of copper were deposited by a current of $0\cdot400$ ampere which passed for 1600 seconds.

   (i) How many coulombs of electricity were passed?   C(1)

  (ii) How many coulombs would be required to liberate one mole of copper(II) ions?   C(2)

 (iii) How many electrons are required to convert one copper(II) ion into a copper atom?   C(1)

 (iv) How many electrons would be required to convert one mole of copper(II) ions into one mole of copper atoms? Express your answer in terms of L.   C(1)

  (v) What is the total charge in coulombs carried by the electrons in your answer to (iv)?   C(1)

 (vi) What is the value of L?   H(2)

(b) It was found that in a particular experiment 2 g of radium emitted $3\cdot7 \times 10^{10}$ alpha particles each second. In a second experiment it was found that $2\cdot32 \times 10^{-4}\,cm^3$ of helium (measured at s.t.p.) were collected in 48 hours.

   (i) How many alpha particles were emitted in 48 hours?   C(2)

  (ii) How many moles of helium were contained in $2\cdot32 \times 10^{-4}\,cm^3$? C(2)

 (iii) What is the value of L?   C(2)

(c) Why do the values in (a)(vi) and (b)(iii) differ?   H(1)

Total   15 marks

4 The determination of relative atomic masses

The mass spectrometer is used to determine the relative masses of nuclides and their relative abundances. The instrument performs three main functions:

(1) The ionization of the sample

(2) The separation of ions in terms of their mass-to-charge ratio

(3) The collection of ions in terms of their relative abundance and relative masses

(a) What do you understand by the term 'nuclide'?   K(1)

(b) (i) How are the ions formed in the instrument?   K(1)

    (ii) Are these ions usually negatively or positively charged?   K(1)

(c) After ionization the ions are accelerated. How is this achieved?   K(1)

(d) The ions, after being accelerated, are diverted into circular paths by a magnetic field. If the ion of ^{35}Cl and the ion of ^{37}Cl are placed in a magnetic field, which ion will have the greatest radius of curvature?   H(1)

(e) How is it possible to obtain the relative abundance of the ions?   K(1)

(f) When a sample of rubidium was analysed in a mass spectrometer the following mass spectrum was obtained:

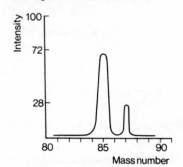

(i) Why do two peaks occur on the mass spectrum?   C(1)

(ii) Why do you think that one peak has a greater area than the other?   C(1)

(iii) What does the term 'relative atomic mass' mean?   K(1)

(iv) Calculate the relative atomic mass of this sample of rubidium.   H(3)

(g) The mass spectrometer can also be used to identify an unknown structure. Explain how this is achieved taking phenylamine (aniline), $C_6H_5NH_2$, as an example.   H(3)

Total   15 marks

5 The relative molecular mass of a gas

The apparatus shown below was used to determine the relative molecular mass of an acidic gas X.

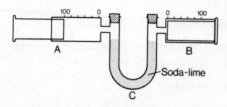

Some of the gas X was drawn into syringe A and then A was connected to the U-tube C. A second syringe, B, was also connected to the U-tube. The gas X in syringe A was slowly forced into the U-tube. The mass of the U-tube was measured both before and after the experiment.

Volume of X taken at 18 °C and one atmosphere pressure	$= 100 \text{ cm}^3$
Mass of U-tube before experiment	$= 107 \cdot 306 \text{ g}$
Mass of U-tube after experiment	$= 107 \cdot 573 \text{ g}$

(a) (i) What is the ideal gas equation? K(1)

 (ii) Assuming X is an ideal gas, calculate the number of moles of X present in 100 cm^3 measured at 18 °C and one atmosphere pressure ($R = 0 \cdot 0821 \text{ atm K}^{-1} \text{ mol}^{-1}$). C(2)

 (iii) Calculate the relative molecular mass of X. C(2)

 (iv) Calculate the volume occupied by one mole of X at 18 °C and one atmosphere pressure. C(2)

 (v) If X consists of only two elements, Y and Z, but is triatomic, what could be its formula? H(1)

(b) (i) What is the function of syringe B? C(1)

 (ii) Describe the sequence of operation of syringes A and B in the experiment. C(2)

 (iii) If the experiment was successfully performed, what would be the final volumes noted in syringes A and B? C(2)

 (iv) What modifications to the apparatus would you suggest to eliminate the use of syringe B? H(2)

 (v) How would you find out whether your modifications in (b)(iv) were successful? H(2)

(c) (i) What modifications should be made to the original apparatus in order to determine the relative molecular mass of an alkaline gas such as ammonia? H(1)

 (ii) Could the original apparatus be used to determine the relative molecular mass of a neutral gas? Give your reasons. H(2)

Total 20 marks

6 Radioactivity

The data relate to the decay of iodine–128.

Time/s	500	2000	3000	4000	6000	8000
Activity /counts per second	146	75	45	27	10	4

(a) (i) Plot a graph of activity (counts per second) against time (seconds). C(2)

    (ii) Determine how long it takes for the activity to drop to one half of the first value (that at 500 s). C(2)

(b) The half-life, $t_{1/2}$, for a radioactive decay process is given by the formula

$$t_{1/2} = \frac{0 \cdot 693}{\lambda}$$

where λ is the radioactive decay constant.

    (i) What are the units of λ if the half-life is in seconds? C(1)

    (ii) What is the value of λ for iodine-128? H(2)

(c) The following is a list of elements near iodine in the periodic table, with their atomic numbers.

Tin	Antimony	Tellurium	Iodine	Xenon	Caesium	Barium
50	51	52	53	54	55	56

    (i) If iodine-128 were to decay by β^- emission, what would be the new element formed? Give your reasons and include a nuclear equation. H(3)

    (ii) If iodine-128 were to decay by α emission, what would be the new element formed? H(1)

(d) (i) State two differences between α and β^- particles. K(2)

    (ii) In order to determine whether the iodine-128 decayed by α or β^- emission, a scientist allowed the iodine-128 to decay in a sealed glass vessel. After several hours he viewed the contents of the vessel spectroscopically. How could this experiment help the scientist to identify the type of emission? H(2)

Total   15 marks

7 Atomic spectra*

The Balmer series is the set of lines observed in the visible region of the atomic spectrum of hydrogen, and can be represented by the equation

$$\frac{1}{\lambda} = R_H \left(\frac{1}{2^2} - \frac{1}{n^2} \right)$$

where λ is the wavelength of the line, n is an integer greater than 2, and R_H is a constant.

The lines in this series occur at the following reciprocal wavelengths.

$\frac{10^4}{\text{(wavelength in metres)}}$	152	205	230	243	251	257	261	263	265

(a) (i) What is the general name given to this type of spectrum?   K(1)

    (ii) Draw an energy transition level diagram to show how the lines of reciprocal wavelength 243 and 257 × 10^4 m^{-1} occur.   H(3)

   (iii) Plot a graph of $1/\lambda$ against $1/n^2$ for the lines of the Balmer series of atomic hydrogen.   C(2)

   (iv) From your graph deduce a value for R_H.   H(2)

    (v) What are the units of the constant R_H?   C(1)

(b) (i) The lines of the spectrum converge at a certain wavelength. What is the value of n when the lines converge?   H(1)

   (ii) What is the significance of this convergence limit?   C(1)

   (iii) How can the ionization energy of an atom be found from convergence data?   C(2)

   (iv) Can the ionization energy for the hydrogen atom in its ground state be found from the Balmer series? Give your reasons.   H(2)

Total   15 marks

8 Electronic structure

The following table gives the electronic configuration of elements in two groups of the periodic table.

Group X		Group Y	
Element	Configuration	Element	Configuration
A	$1s^2\ 2s^2$	E	$1s^2\ 2s^2\ 2p^5$
B	$1s^2\ 2s^2\ 2p^6\ 3s^2$	F	$1s^2\ 2s^2\ 2p^6\ 3s^2\ 3p^5$
C	$1s^2\ 2s^2\ 2p^6\ 3s^2\ 3p^6\ 4s^2$	G	_____
D	_____		

(a) In which groups of the periodic table do elements in group

    (i) X belong?   C (1)

    (ii) Y belong?   C (1)

(b) What are the electronic configurations of

    (i) the next element in group X, i.e. element D?   H (1)

    (ii) the next element in group Y, i.e. element G?   H (1)

(c) The principal quantum numbers of an atom give only a very brief description of the electronic configuration of the atom.

    (i) How many principal quantum numbers are used to describe the electronic configuration in F?   C (1)

    (ii) What is the maximum number of electrons that can be held in the second quantum level?   C (1)

(d) Subsidiary quantum numbers amplify the principal quantum numbers and are designated by the letters s, p, d, etc. What is the maximum number of electrons in the d orbital?   K (1)

(e) What further quantum number(s) is/are required to fully describe an electron?   K (2)

(f)   (i) State Hund's rule of maximum multiplicity.   K (1)

    (ii) How many paired electrons are there in B and in F?   H (2)

(g) If A and E were made to react together,

    (i) would you expect the compound to be ionic or covalent? Give your reasons.   H (2)

    (ii) what would be the formula of the compound in terms of A and E?   H (1)

Total   15 marks

9 Ionization energies

Below are listed the five successive ionization energies of five elements in one group of the periodic table. The letters are not the symbols for the elements, but the elements are in order of increasing atomic number.

Element	Ionization energies /kJ mol^{-1}				
	1	2	3	4	5
V	1090	2400	4600	6200	37 800
W	790	1600	3200	4400	16 100
X	760	1500	3300	4400	9 000
Y	710	1400	2900	3900	7 000
Z	720	1500	3100	4100	6 600

(a) (i) Plot a graph of the number of electrons removed from the atom W against the ionization energy.   C(2)

(ii) Explain why there appears to be a large jump in ionization energy in going from the fourth ionization to the fifth.   H(2)

(iii) State in which group of the periodic table the elements V to Z appear.   C(2)

(b) (i) Explain why there is a decrease in each particular ionization energy on descending the group.   C(2)

(ii) Would you expect the value of the sixth ionization energy to be greater than the fifth? Give your reasons.   H(2)

(c) The element V (atomic number 6) is unable to form cations V^{4+} in compounds.

(i) What is the electronic configuration of the V^{4+} ion?   C(1)

(ii) Can you suggest why the cations V^{4+} are not found in compounds?   H(2)

(iii) What type of bonding would you expect between the element V and chlorine? Give your reasons.   H(2)

Total   15 marks

10 Molecular shape

A principle developed by Sidgwick and Powell states that 'charge clouds in the outer shell of an atom in a molecule stay as far away from each other as possible'. The rule can be applied to both bonding clouds and non-bonding clouds, and can be used to determine molecular shape. This aspect was fully developed by Nyholm and Gillespie in 1957.

(a) (i) What do you understand by the term 'charge cloud'?   C(1)

   (ii) What do you understand by the term 'non-bonding cloud'?   C(2)

(b) Look at the following diagrams of shapes of simple molecules.

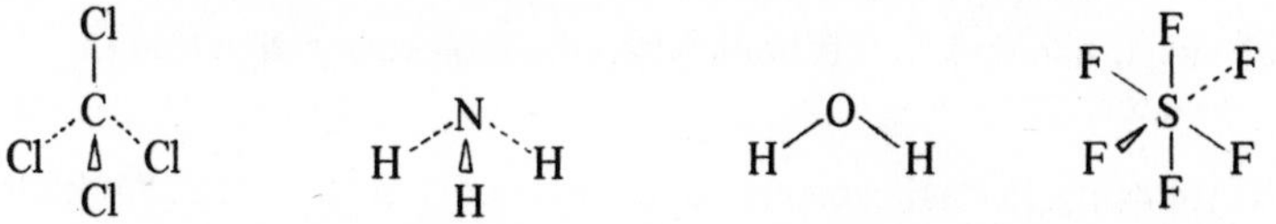

     (A)   (B)   (C)   (D)

  (i) Which one of the above has the greatest number of bonding clouds?   C(1)

  (ii) Which one of the above has the greatest number of non-bonding clouds?   H(1)

  (iii) Draw a diagram to show the position of non-bonding clouds in C.   C(1)

  (iv) What is the name of the shape on which structure D is based?   K(1)

  (v) The ammonia molecule (structure B) is based on a tetrahedron. Explain why the structure is not triangular and planar.   C(2)

  (vi) Name a triatomic molecule which is triangular and planar.   K(1)

(c) The atomic number of nitrogen is 7 and of hydrogen 1.

  (i) What is the electronic configuration of nitrogen?   C(1)

  (ii) Draw a 'dot-and-cross' diagram to show the electron arrangement in the ion NH_2^-.   H(2)

  (iii) What shape would you expect this ion to adopt? Give your reasons.   H(2)

Total   15 marks

11 Dipole moments

The hydrogen chloride molecule can be written as

$$\overset{\delta+}{H}—\overset{\delta-}{Cl}$$

(a) (i) What do the symbols $\delta+$ and $\delta-$ represent?   K (2)

    (ii) What physical property indicates that there is a charge separation in the molecule?   K (1)

   (iii) What properties of the elements, hydrogen and chloride, account for the formation of this bond type?   C (2)

   (iv) What happens to this bond when the molecule is dissolved in water?   C (2)

(b) The following list indicates the dipole moments of some group V hydrides.

$NH_3 = 5.0 \times 10^{-30}$ C m

$PH_3 = 2.0 \times 10^{-30}$ C m

$AsH_3 = 0.7 \times 10^{-30}$ C m

    (i) Explain what you understand by the term 'dipole moment'.   K (2)

    (ii) What is the molecular shape of these molecules?   K (1)

   (iii) Explain why the dipole moment decreases along the series.   C (2)

   (iv) How do you think the dipole moment will vary along the series PCl_3, PBr_3, PI_3?   H (2)

    (v) Name a tetraatomic molecule with zero dipole moment.   K (1)

Total   15 marks

12 Ionic radii

Ionic radii (pm) of some of group I, II, and III metals are given below.

Group I		Group II		Group III	
Li^+	68	Be^{2+}	30	B^{3+}	16
Na^+	98	Mg^{2+}	65	Al^{3+}	45
K^+	133	Ca^{2+}	94	Ga^{3+}	62
Rb^+	148	Sr^{2+}	110		
Cs^+	167				

(a) (i) Account for the increase in size on descending the groups.   K (2)

    (ii) Account for the decrease in size in moving from group I to group III.   K (2)

(b) What are the main factors which determine whether an ionic compound will be formed?   K (2)

(c) (i) Which ion in group II would be formed most readily?   C (1)

    (ii) Which of all the ions listed would be the most difficult to form? Give your reasons.   H (2)

(d) Large anions are polarized by the presence of small cations. A rough measure of the polarizing power is given by the ratio of ionic charge to ionic radius.

    (i) What is meant by the term 'polarizing power'?   C (2)

    (ii) On the basis of this polarizing power, which ion in group II would be expected to resemble Li^+ and to resemble Al^{3+} most closely?   H (2)

    (iii) Place the following compounds in order of increasing ionic character: $LiCl$, $CaCl_2$, $CsCl$. Give your reasons.   H (2)

Total   15 marks

13 Solids

The following diagram represents the crystalline cubic structure of iron at room temperature (293 K).

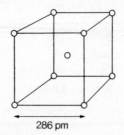

286 pm

(a) Describe briefly how such structures are determined.   K (4)

(b)   (i) What is the name given to the above structure?   C (1)

    (ii) What is the coordination number of the central iron atom in the given structure?   C (1)

    (iii) The atomic radii of atoms can be determined by measuring the side of the cubic structure. Calculate the radius of the iron atom, stating any assumptions you make.   H (2)

(c) Iron can also exist in another crystalline form at 1380 K – a face-centred cubic structure of side 363 pm.

    (i) Draw a diagram to show this structure.   C (2)

    (ii) How many nearest neighbours does a single iron atom have in this structure?   C (1)

(d)   (i) Which of the two structures for iron has the most efficient packing of atoms?   H (1)

    (ii) Which of the two structures would have the lower density?   H (1)

(e) How is it possible to obtain a value for the Avogadro constant L from the dimensions of the unit cell and the number of particles it contains?   C (4)

(f) Explain briefly how a metal such as iron is able to conduct electricity. K (3)

Total   20 marks

14 Liquids

Any theory of the liquid state has to account for many factors, e.g. entropy, enthalpy, viscosity, compressibility, and volume changes, in forming a solid. No theory has yet been produced which adequately accounts for all these factors.

One theory by Eyring considers a liquid being composed of molecules and free spaces. The molecules move about at random both singly and in clusters.

Relative atomic masses: H = 1, O = 16

(a) The volume of a water molecule is estimated at 2.9×10^{-23} cm^3.

   (i) What is the volume of one mole of water molecules
   ($L = 6 \times 10^{23}$ mol^{-1})?   C (1)

   (ii) What is the volume taken up by one mole of water if the density of
   water is 1.0 g cm^{-3}?   C (1)

   (iii) Account for the difference in volume between the volume in
   (a)(i) and (a)(ii).   C (2)

   (iv) Calculate the percentage decrease in volume.   C (2)

(b) The following is a list of the boiling points of some triatomic hydrides.

Hydride	H_2O	H_2S	H_2Se	H_2Te
Boiling point /K	373	213	232	271
Enthalpy of vaporization /kJ mol^{-1}	41	18.7	19.3	23.2
Relative molecular mass	18	34	81	130

   (i) How is vapour pressure explained on the kinetic theory?   K (2)

   (ii) Sketch a graph to show how the vapour pressure varies with
   temperature.   C (1)

   (iii) Why do liquids boil when heated sufficiently?   K (1)

   (iv) What do you understand by the term 'enthalpy of vaporization'?
                                                                           K (2)

   (v) Why does water have a higher boiling point and a higher enthalpy of
   vaporization per mole than the other liquids?   C (3)

   (vi) Suggest another property which may show a similar trend.   H (1)

   (vii) How would you expect the entropy to change when there is a phase
   change from liquid into vapour? Give your reasons.   K (2)

   (viii) For which of the liquids listed would you expect the largest entropy
   change in the phase change, liquid to vapour?   H (2)

Total   20 marks

15 Gases*

The following graph represents the relative distribution of molecular velocities in oxygen at a temperature of 250 K.

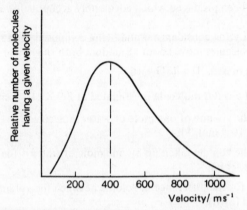

(a) Redraw the above diagram and include two further curves for oxygen, labelling them 100 K and 500 K, which show the distribution at these temperatures.   C (4)

(b) (i) Redraw the above diagram and include the curve for the distribution of velocities in nitrogen at a temperature of 250 K.   H (2)

     (ii) At what temperature would the relative number of molecules of nitrogen having a velocity of $400 \, \mathrm{m \, s^{-1}}$ be the same as that for oxygen at 250 K (relative atomic masses: N = 14, O = 16)?   H (3)

(c) (i) State four assumptions on which the kinetic theory of ideal gases is based.   K (4)

     (ii) Which of these assumptions are invalid for a non-ideal gas?   K (2)

(d) The expression $pV = \frac{1}{3} Nm\overline{c^2}$ for an ideal gas can be obtained from kinetic theory.

     (i) What do the symbols N, m, and $\overline{c^2}$ stand for?   K (2)

     (ii) Using this expression and the ideal gas equation, show that the kinetic energy E_m for one mole of gas is $E_m = \frac{3}{2} RT$ where R is the gas constant and T the thermodynamic temperature.   H (3)

Total   20 marks

16 Bond lengths and bond energies

The following table gives some data on carbon–carbon bonds.

Bond	Bond length /pm	Bond energy /kJ mol^{-1}
C–C (ethane)	154	346
C=C (ethene)	134	610
C≡C (ethyne)	121	813
carbon–carbon (benzene)	139	–

(a) Plot a graph of bond energy (vertical axis) against bond length (horizontal axis) and use your graph to estimate the bond energy in benzene.　　C (3)

(b) Why do you think the bond energy increases as the bond length decreases?　　K (2)

(c) Why is the bond length in benzene intermediate between that in ethane and ethene?　　C (2)

(d) On the basis of your answer in (c) predict the (C–C) bond length in the following molecule for the two bonds named below.

$$
\begin{array}{cccccc}
1 & 2 & 3 & 4 & 5 & 6
\end{array}
$$
$$CH_3-CH=CH-CH=CH-CH_3$$

  (i)　carbon(2)–carbon(3)　　H (1)

  (ii)　carbon(3)–carbon(4)　　H (1)

(e) The following table gives some data on carbon–halide bonds.

Bond	Bond length /pm	Electronegativity difference (carbon–halide)
C–F	132	1·5
C–Cl	177	0·5
C–Br	194	0·3
C–I	214	0·0

  (i)　What is meant by the term 'electronegativity'?　　K (1)

  (ii)　Why do you think that the bond length increases with decreasing electronegativity difference?　　K (2)

(iii) State another factor which would cause the bond length to increase along the series C—F, C—Cl, C—Br, C—I. K (1)

(iv) Predict how the bond energy would vary along the series C—F, C—Cl, C—Br, C—I. Give your reasons. H (2)

Total   15 marks

17 Enthalpies of formation and combustion

The following table gives some information on the enthalpies of formation $(\Delta H_f^\ominus)$ and combustion $(\Delta H_c^\ominus)$ of some hydrocarbons of molecular formula C_4H_8.

Hydrocarbon	$\Delta H_f^\ominus$/kJ mol^{-1}	$\Delta H_c^\ominus$/kJ mol^{-1}
cyclobutane	−7·1	−
trans-But-2-ene	−12·0	−2700
cis-But-2-ene	−7·0	−2710
But-1-ene	−	−2720

(a) Draw the structural formulae of
   (i) cyclobutane. C (1)
   (ii) *trans*-but-2-ene. C (1)

(b) (i) What do you understand by the term 'enthalpy of formation of a compound'? K (2)
   (ii) Suggest why there is a difference in the values for the standard enthalpies of formation of *trans*- and *cis*-but-2-ene. H (2)

(c) (i) Write an equation for the combustion of cyclobutane in oxygen. C (1)
   (ii) If the standard enthalpies of formation of carbon dioxide and water are −390 and −240 kJ mol^{-1} respectively, calculate the enthalpy of combustion of cyclobutane. C (2)
   (iii) Which one of the four hydrocarbons listed would be the best fuel? Give your reasons. C (2)

(d) The following table gives some data for the energies required to break three different bonds.

Bond	Energy /kJ mol^{-1}
C−H	400
C=C	600
C−C	350

   (i) Using these data, calculate the enthalpy of atomization of but-1-ene. H (2)
   (ii) Which of the four hydrocarbons listed is the most stable with respect to its elements? Give your reasons. H (2)

Total   15 marks

18 The Born-Haber cycle

The following figure illustrates a Born–Haber cycle for a possible rare gas compound $Ne^+ X^-$, where X is a halogen atom (fluorine, chlorine, bromine, or iodine).

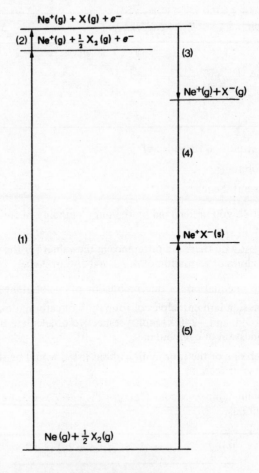

(a) State Hess' law of constant heat summation.   K (2)

(b) What are the names given to the individual steps (1) to (5)?   C (5)

(c) (i) Name the halogen for which the enthalpy change (2) has the smallest value.   K (1)

    (ii) Name the halogen for which the enthalpy change (3) has the largest value.   K (1)

(d) Use the following information (in $kJ\,mol^{-1}$) for neon and the halogen chlorine.

$$Ne(g) \rightarrow Ne^+(g) + e^- \qquad \Delta H = +2088$$
$$\tfrac{1}{2}Cl_2(g) \rightarrow Cl(g) \qquad \Delta H = +121$$
$$Cl(g) + e^- \rightarrow Cl^-(g) \qquad \Delta H = -365$$
$$Ne(g) + \tfrac{1}{2}Cl_2(g) \rightarrow Ne^+Cl^-(s) \qquad \Delta H = +1091$$

(i) Determine the value of step (4) using a graphical method.   C(4)

(ii) Comment on this value as to the possibility of formation of $Ne^+Cl^-(s)$.   H(2)

Total   15 marks

19 Equilibrium: gaseous

Consider the equilibrium which takes place in a closed container between dinitrogen tetraoxide and nitrogen dioxide,

$$N_2O_4(g) \rightleftharpoons 2NO_2(g)$$

(a) If the equilibrium constant K_p for this reaction at 300 K is 1.40×10^{-1} atm.

    (i) Derive an expression for the equilibrium constant K_p in terms of partial pressures and the total pressure P.   H(2)

   (ii) If one mole of N_2O_4 was taken initially under a total pressure of 2 atmospheres, how much nitrogen dioxide would be present at equilibrium?   H(2)

  (iii) If the total pressure was then increased to 4 atmospheres, how much dinitrogen tetraoxide would be present at equilibrium?   H(2)

  (iv) What is the effect of adding an additional mole of dinitrogen tetraoxide to the equilibrium at 300 K?   H(2)

(b) If the temperature of the system in (a)(ii) is raised to 600 K, the value of K_p is found to be 1.80×10^4 atm.

    (i) Is the reaction exo- or endothermic? Give your reasons.   C(2)

   (ii) What is the effect of this increase in temperature on the equilibrium concentration of nitrogen dioxide?   H(2)

(c)   (i) How does the rate of the forward reaction compare with that of the backward reaction at equilibrium?   K(1)

   (ii) What effect does a catalyst have on the rate of the forward reaction at equilibrium?   K(1)

  (iii) What effect does a catalyst have on the equilibrium concentration of nitrogen dioxide?   K(1)

Total   15 marks

20 Equilibrium: solid-liquid

A student studied the following equilibrium system

$$Ag^+(aq) + Fe^{2+}(aq) \rightleftharpoons Fe^{3+}(aq) + Ag(s)$$

$30 \, cm^3$ of iron(II) sulphate(VI) (concentration $0.10 \, mol \, dm^{-3}$) was mixed with $10 \, cm^3$ of silver nitrate(V) (concentration $0.10 \, mol \, dm^{-3}$) and $20 \, cm^3$ of nitric(V) acid (concentration $0.01 \, mol \, dm^{-3}$). After 20 minutes the mixture had reached equilibrium and the solution was filtered. The precipitate was then washed twice with distilled water, all washings being added to the filtrate. $5 \, cm^3$ of iron(III) nitrate(V) (concentration $1 \, mol \, dm^{-3}$) were then added to the filtrate. The filtrate was then titrated with potassium thiocyanate, KCNS (concentration $0.10 \, mol \, dm^{-3}$), until the mixture took on a permanent red-brown tinge. The precipitate which formed during the titration began to flocculate just before the end point. It was found that only $1.80 \, cm^3$ of the potassium thiocyanate were required.

(a) Is the equilibrium of a heterogeneous or homogeneous type?   K (1)

(b) (i) Why do you think that nitric(V) acid was added to the mixture? C (1)

    (ii) What was the precipitate formed when equilibrium had been reached?   C (1)

    (iii) Why was the precipitate washed twice?   C (1)

    (iv) Why were $5 \, cm^3$ of iron(III) nitrate(V) added to the filtrate?   C (1)

(c) (i) Write an ionic equation describing the formation of a precipitate when potassium thiocyanate is added to the filtrate.   C (1)

    (ii) Why does the solution turn red-brown at the end point?   C (1)

(d) (i) What is the initial concentration (in $mol \, dm^{-3}$) of the Fe^{2+} in the initial *mixture* of solutions?   C (1)

    (ii) What is the initial concentration of Ag^+ (in $mol \, dm^{-3}$) in the initial *mixture* of solutions?   C (1)

    (iii) What is the equilibrium concentration of Ag^+ (in $mol \, dm^{-3}$)?   C (1)

    (iv) What is the equilibrium concentration of Fe^{3+} (in $mol \, dm^{-3}$)?   C (1)

    (v) What is the equilibrium concentration of Fe^{2+} (in $mol \, dm^{-3}$)?   C (2)

(e) (i) If the equilibrium constant is given by the expression

$$K_c = -\frac{[Fe^{3+}]}{[Fe^{2+}] \, [Ag^+]}$$

where the square brackets indicate the concentrations in $mol \, dm^{-3}$ of the components at equilibrium, calculate a value for K_c.   H (2)

    (ii) What information about the position of equilibrium can be deduced from the value of K_c.   C(1)

    (iii) How would you confirm that K_c was in fact constant?   H(2)

(f)   (i) Why is the concentration of the silver not included in the equilibrium expression?   C(1)

    (ii) How could the concentration of the silver be determined, if it were required?   H(1)

Total   20 marks

21 Equilibrium: partitioning

A student investigated the equilibrium of ammonia between water and trichloromethane (chloroform) in a mixture. He shook 50 cm^3 portions of aqueous ammonia of various concentrations with 50 cm^3 of trichloromethane for about 3 minutes each. At the end of this time he separated the two layers and titrated each with dilute hydrochloric acid using a suitable indicator. He plotted a graph of his results as shown below.

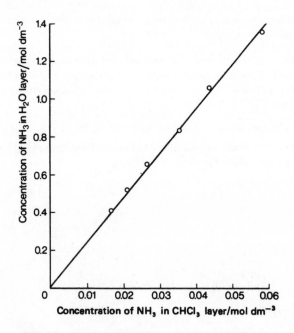

(a) (i) Suggest why the ammonia is soluble in both water and trichloromethane.   C (2)

    (ii) Which is the most effective solvent for ammonia, water or trichloromethane?   C (1)

(b) From the linear nature of the graph the student thought that the equilibrium could be represented by the equation

$$[NH_3(H_2O)] = K [NH_3(CHCl_3)]$$

where the square brackets indicate the concentrations in mol dm^{-3} of the ammonia in the stated solvents at equilibrium.

    (i) What is the name usually given to the constant K?   K (1)

    (ii) What are the units of K in this case?   C(1)

    (iii) From the graph, obtain a value for K.   H(2)

(c) In a typical experiment, $50 \, cm^3$ of aqueous ammonia (concentration $1 \, mol \, dm^{-3}$) were shaken with $50 \, cm^3$ of trichloromethane. Assume a value for K of 25.

    (i) What would be the concentration (in $mol \, dm^{-3}$) of the ammonia in the trichloromethane layer?   H(2)

    (ii) How many moles of ammonia would be present in $50 \, cm^3$ of trichloromethane?   C(1)

    (iii) What volume of hydrochloric acid (concentration $0 \cdot 1 \, mol \, dm^{-3}$) would be required to neutralize the ammonia in the trichloromethane?   C(1)

(d) After shaking the two liquids with ammonia solution in an experiment, the liquids are allowed to stand, and an aqueous solution of copper(II) sulphate(VI) is then added carefully to the water layer, before titration with the acid.

    (i) What changes would you see in the water layer?   K(2)

    (ii) What do you think this addition of copper(II) sulphate(VI) would have on the value of K determined?   H(2)

Total   15 marks

22 Acidity and alkalinity*

You are supplied with the following information concerning a number of organic acids.

Acid	Formula	Ionization constant K_a /mol dm^{-3}
Ethanoic	CH_3-COOH	1.7×10^{-5}
Chloroethanoic	$ClCH_2-COOH$	1.3×10^{-3}
Dichloroethanoic	$Cl_2CH-COOH$	5.0×10^{-2}
Trichloroethanoic	$Cl_3C-COOH$	2.3×10^{-1}

Ionic product of water $K_w = 1.0 \times 10^{-14}$ mol^2 dm^{-6}

(a) (i) Which of the above acids is the strongest?   C(1)

    (ii) What is the pK_a value for ethanoic acid?   C(2)

    (iii) Why is the ionization constant of chloroethanoic acid larger than that for ethanoic acid?   C(2)

(b) (i) Give an equation for the ionization reaction of dichloroethanoic acid in water.   C(1)

    (ii) Calculate the hydrogen ion concentration of an aqueous solution of dichloroethanoic acid (concentration 0.01 mol dm^{-3}).   C(2)

    (iii) What do you understand by the term 'pH'?   K(1)

    (iv) Calculate the pH of an aqueous solution of dichloroethanoic acid (concentration 0.01 mol dm^{-3}).   C(3)

(c) (i) What is the hydroxide ion concentration of an aqueous solution of chloroethanoic acid (concentration 0.001 mol dm^{-3})?   C(2)

    (ii) If this solution were further diluted, what is the limiting value of the hydroxide ion concentration?   H(2)

    (iii) What volume of sodium hydroxide (concentration 0.1 mol dm^{-3}) would be required to produce a neutral solution in 100 cm^3 of chloroethanoic acid (concentration 0.001 mol dm^{-3})?   H(2)

    (iv) If it were required to obtain this answer volumetrically, suggest a suitable indicator for the titration. Give your reasons.   H(2)

Total   20 marks

23 pH and buffers

The equilibrium for propanoic (propionic) acid in water can be written

$$C_2H_5COOH(aq) \rightleftharpoons C_2H_5COO^-(aq) + H^+(aq)$$

(a) (i) Write down an expression for K_a, the ionization constant, in terms of the concentration of each component. C(1)

(ii) Show that the pH of a solution is related to K_a by the expression

$$pH = -\log K_a - \log \frac{[C_2H_5COOH(aq)]}{[C_2H_5COO^-(aq)]}$$ C(2)

(b) What do you understand by the term 'buffer solution'? K(2)

(c) $100 \, cm^3$ of propanoic acid (concentration $0\cdot1 \, mol \, dm^{-3}$) were mixed with $100 \, cm^3$ of sodium propanoate (propionate) (concentration $0\cdot05 \, mol \, dm^{-3}$) in order to make a buffer solution (K_a for propanoic acid = $1\cdot3 \times 10^{-5}$ $mol \, dm^{-3}$).

(i) Why was sodium propanoate chosen for the buffer solution and not, say, sodium chloride? C(1)

(ii) Calculate the pH of the buffer solution so formed. H(3)

(d) In order to determine the effectiveness of the buffer solution in (c), the following two experiments were performed.

(i) $10 \, cm^3$ of hydrochloric acid (concentration $0\cdot1 \, mol \, dm^{-3}$) were added to $100 \, cm^3$ of the buffer solution from (c). What will be the new pH of the solution? H(2)

(ii) $10 \, cm^3$ of hydrochloric acid (concentration $0\cdot1 \, mol \, dm^{-3}$) were added to $100 \, cm^3$ of the propanoic acid (concentration $0\cdot1 \, mol \, dm^{-3}$). What is the pH of this solution? H(2)

(iii) On the basis of your findings in the two previous experiments, comment on the effectiveness of the buffer solution. H(2)

Total 15 marks

24 Indicators

The following table gives the colours of three indicators in $10\,cm^3$ portions of hydrochloric acid at varying concentrations.

Indicator	Hydrochloric acid concentration /mol dm^{-3}						
	10^{-1}	10^{-2}	10^{-3}	10^{-4}	10^{-5}	10^{-6}	10^{-7}
Thymol blue	R	O	Y	Y	Y	Y	Y
Bromocresol green	Y	Y	Y	G	B	B	B
Bromocresol purple	Y	Y	Y	Y	Y	G	V

R = red, O = orange, Y = yellow, G = green, B = blue, V = violet

(a) What is the effective pH range of each indicator? C(3)

(b) (i) Which of the above indicators is the strongest acid? C(1)

   (ii) What is the approximate pK_a of bromocresol purple? Give reasons for your answer. H(2)

(c) (i) What would be the colour of thymol blue indicator in hydrochloric acid solution (concentration $1\ mol\ dm^{-3}$)? C(2)

   (ii) What would be the colour of bromocresol purple in sodium hydroxide solution (concentration $0.001\ mol\ dm^{-3}$)? C(2)

(d) When $10\,cm^3$ portions of trichloroethanoic (trichloroacetic) acid (concentration $0.1\ mol\ dm^{-3}$) were added to $5\,cm^3$ of sodium hydroxide solution (concentration $0.1\ mol\ dm^{-3}$) containing two drops of each indicator, the following colours were obtained.

Thymol blue	Bromocresol green	Bromocresol purple
red	yellow	yellow

   (i) Deduce the approximate pK_a of trichloroethanoic acid. H(3)

   (ii) State, giving your reasons, which indicator you would choose for titrating trichloroethanoic acid (concentration $0.1\ mol\ dm^{-3}$) with sodium hydroxide solution (concentration $0.1\ mol\ dm^{-3}$). H(2)

Total   15 marks

25 Kinetics: reaction orders

Some experimental data obtained from a reaction between hydrogen and nitrogen oxide at 1000 K are as follows.

Initial concentration of H_2 /mol m^{-3}	Initial concentration of NO /mol m^{-3}	Initial rate /mol m^{-3} s^{-1}
5·0	1·0	0·4
5·0	2·0	1·6
5·0	3·0	3·6
1·0	5·0	2·0
2·0	5·0	4·0
3·0	5·0	6·0

(a) (i) What is the order of the reaction with respect to the hydrogen? H(1)

(ii) What is the order of the reaction with respect to the nitrogen oxide? H(1)

(iii) What is the experimental rate law for this reaction? C(2)

(b) (i) What are the units of the specific rate constant for this reaction? C(1)

(ii) Calculate the specific rate constant at the temperature of the reaction. H(2)

(c) (i) Predict the initial rate of the reaction if
$$[NO] = [H_2] = 4·0 \times 10^{-3} \, \text{mol dm}^{-3}$$
H(2)

(ii) What would be the effect of raising the temperature by 20 K on this initial reaction rate? C(2)

(d) The stoichiometric equation for this reaction is
$$2H_2(g) + 2NO(g) \rightarrow 2H_2O(g) + N_2(g)$$
Suggest a possible mechanism for the reaction. H(4)

Total   15 marks

26 Kinetics: organic

Hughes and Ingold (1935–40) examined nucleophilic substitution and, in particular, the rate of hydrolysis of bromoalkanes in alkaline aqueous ethanol at 325 K according to the equation

$$HO^- + R-Br \rightarrow HO-R + Br^-$$

Investigation of the kinetics of this reaction showed that there are two extreme types, of which one was

$$\text{Rate} = k \ [R-Br] \ [OH^-]$$

(a) What do you understand by the term 'nucleophilic substitution'? K (2)

(b) (i) What is the overall order in the above rate equation? C (1)

   (ii) The reaction given above is thought to proceed via a transition state or 'activated complex'. Write down a structural formula for the activated complex. H (2)

   (iii) Draw a labelled diagram of an 'energy profile' for the above reaction. H (3)

(c) (i) Write down an expression for the rate of reaction for the other type of hydrolysis. C (2)

   (ii) What is the effect of doubling the OH^- concentration on this reaction rate? C (1)

(d) Hughes and Ingold gave the following data for a series of experiments on the hydrolysis of certain alkyl bromides.

Rate constant ($\times 10^5$)	CH_3-Br	C_2H_5-Br	$CH_3-CH(Br)-CH_3$	$(CH_3)_3C-Br$
Second-order	2140	710	4·7	
First-order			0·24	1010

   (i) What are the units for the first-order rate constant and the second-order rate constant? C (2)

   (ii) Suggest why the molecule $CH_3-CH(Br)-CH_3$ should have both a first-order and a second-order rate constant. H (2)

   (iii) Suggest a mechanism for the hydrolysis of $(CH_3)_3C-Br$. H (3)

Total   18 marks

27 Kinetics: effect of temperature

The logarithmic form of the Arrhenius equation

$$\log k = \log A - \frac{E}{2 \cdot 3\,RT}$$

describes the variation of the rate constant k of a chemical reaction with temperature, where T is the thermodynamic temperature, R the gas constant ($R = 8 \cdot 3\,\mathrm{J\,K^{-1}\,mol^{-1}}$), and A and E are constants for a particular reaction.

(a) Explain concisely the significance of the constants A and E.   C(4)

(b) The thermal decomposition of benzenediazonium chloride ($C_6H_5N{\equiv}N^+Cl^-$) was studied over a range of temperatures and the following data obtained.

Temperature /K	(Temperature)$^{-1}$ /K^{-1}	log k /k in s^{-1}
277	$3 \cdot 61 \times 10^{-3}$	$0 \cdot 17$
295	$3 \cdot 38 \times 10^{-3}$	$1 \cdot 63$
307	$3 \cdot 25 \times 10^{-3}$	$2 \cdot 31$
322	$3 \cdot 10 \times 10^{-3}$	$3 \cdot 14$

(i) Write an equation for the thermal decomposition of benzenediazonium chloride.   C(1)

(ii) Plot a graph of log k against $1/T$.   C(3)

(iii) From the graph, calculate a value for E, clearly stating the units of E.   H(2)

(iv) Calculate the value of A.   H(2)

(v) Draw a suitable piece of apparatus you could use to study the decomposition of benzenediazonium chloride at various temperatures, say between 273 and 373 K.   H(3)

Total   15 marks

28 Electrochemistry: cells

The following diagram refers to an electrolytic cell.

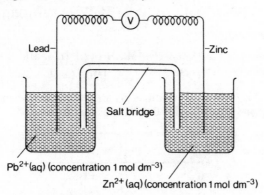

$$Pb^{2+}(aq)/Pb(s) \;\; E^{\ominus} = -0.14 \text{ V}$$
$$Zn^{2+}(aq)/Zn(s) \;\; E^{\ominus} = -0.76 \text{ V}$$

(a) (i) What is meant by the term 'salt bridge', and what is its function? K (2)

    (ii) Do the electrons in the circuit flow from the lead to the zinc or vice versa?   C (1)

    (iii) What is the sign of the left-hand electrode?   H (1)

(b) (i) Which of the species listed above is the strongest oxidizing agent? C (1)

    (ii) What is the cell voltage?   H (1)

    (iii) Write an ionic equation for the reaction which takes place.   C (1)

    (iv) What is the value of ΔG for this reaction ($F = 96\,500$ C mol^{-1})? H (2)

(c) A piece of magnesium ribbon was placed in the beaker containing lead ions while the above circuit is in operation. The magnesium was not in contact with the lead plate.

$$Mg^{2+}(aq)/Mg(s) \;\; E^{\ominus} = -2.34 \text{ V}$$

    (i) Describe what would be seen in the beaker containing lead ions. H (1)

(d) (i) What do you understand by the term 'standard electrode potential'?   K (1)

    (ii) Draw a diagram to show how the standard electrode potential could be determined for the electrode $Pb^{2+}(aq)/Pb(s)$.   C (2)

Total 15 marks

29 Electrochemistry: electrode potentials*

At room temperature the electrode potential E for the system

$$[MnO_4^-(aq) + 8H^+(aq)], [Mn^{2+}(aq) + 4H_2O(l)]/Pt$$

is given by the equation

$$E = E^\ominus + \frac{0.059}{5} \log \frac{[MnO_4^-(aq)] \; [H^+(aq)]^8}{[Mn^{2+}(aq)]}$$

where $E^\ominus = 1.51$ V. E values at various pH are given below when $[MnO_4^-(aq)] = 0.01$ mol dm^{-3} and $[Mn^{2+}(aq)] = 0.0001$ mol dm^{-3}.

pH	E/V
0	+1·52
3	+1·24
7	+0·83

(a) To what does the symbol $E^\ominus$ refer?　　　　　　　　　　　K (1)

(b) What would be the electrode potential of the cell at pH 1, when the manganate(VII) ion concentration is 0·01 mol dm^{-3} and the manganese(II) ion concentration is 0·001 mol dm^{-3}.　　　H (3)

(c) At which of the pH values listed is the solution the strongest oxidizing agent?　　　　　　　　　　　　　　　　　　　　　C (1)

(d) Look at the following electrode systems:

$$Cl_2(aq), 2Cl^-(aq)/Pt \qquad E^\ominus = +1.36 \text{ V}$$
$$Br_2(aq), 2Br^-(aq)/Pt \qquad E^\ominus = +1.09 \text{ V}$$
$$I_2(aq), 2I^-(aq)/Pt \qquad E^\ominus = +0.54 \text{ V}$$

　(i) Which of the species listed is the strongest reducing agent?　　C (1)

　(ii) Explain why it is possible to oxidize chloride ions to chlorine using potassium manganate(VII) at pH 0, but not in solution at pH 3.　H (2)

　(iii) Predict whether bromine can be formed by adding bromide ions to potassium manganate(VII) solution containing ethanoic acid (pH 3). Give a reason for your answer.　　　　　　　　　　　H (2)

(e) Consider the two half-reactions:

$$Mn^{2+}(aq) + 4H_2O(l) \rightarrow MnO_4^-(aq) + 8H^+(aq) + 5e^-$$
$$BiO_3^-(aq) + 6H^+(aq) + 2e^- \rightarrow Bi^{3+}(aq) + 3H_2O(l)$$

34

(i) What is the oxidation state of bismuth in the bismuthate ion, BiO_3^-? C(1)

(ii) Write a balanced ionic equation for the reaction between bismuthate ions and manganese(II) ions in acid solution. H(2)

(f) Consider the electrode system

$$[BiO_3^- (aq) + 6H^+(aq)], [Bi^{3+}(aq) + 3H_2O(l)]/Pt \quad E^\ominus = 1.71 \text{ V}$$

(i) What would be the effect of lowering the pH on this system? H(2)

(ii) How would you attempt to measure the cell voltage? H(3)

(iii) What would be the cell voltage produced when an acidified solution of manganese(II) ions was added to bismuthate ions at pH 0? H(2)

Total 20 marks

30 Electrochemistry: conductivity

The electrolytic conductivity κ of a solution in a cell is given by the following formula:

$$\kappa = \frac{Gl}{a}$$

where G is the conductance of the cell and a is the cross-sectional area of the electrodes, separated by a distance l. The conductance of a cell containing an aqueous solution of an electrolyte depends on (1) the number of free ions in the cell, (2) the speed at which the ions move, and (3) the number of charges on each ion.

(a) (i) Often the term $1/a$ is replaced by a cell constant K. What would be the cell constant of a particular cell if it was found that the conductance of the cell containing potassium chloride (concentration 0·10 mol dm^{-3}) is 0·022 S (Ω^{-1}) and the electrolytic conductivity was 0·011 S cm^{-1}? Give the units of K. C(2)

(ii) Assuming no interaction of ions and also square electrodes, calculate the number of free ions *within* the cell. The Avogadro constant is 6×10^{23} mol^{-1}. H(2)

(b) How would you expect the electrolytic conductivity of potassium chloride to vary with concentration? Illustrate your answer with the aid of a graph. K(2)

(c) State three factors which determine the speed of ions. K(3)

(d) One of the uses of conductance measurements is in determining the end point of a precipitation reaction accurately. The graph below shows how the conductance of 20 cm^3 potassium chloride solution varied after additions of various quantities of silver nitrate(V) (concentration 0·1 mol dm^{-3}).

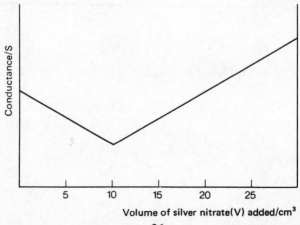

(i) Write an ionic equation for the precipitation reaction.   C(1)

(ii) If the reaction is carried out as a normal titration, name an indicator used to determine the end point.   K(1)

(iii) Explain why the conductance falls slowly before the end point, but rises quickly after.   C(2)

(iv) What is the concentration (in mol dm^{-3}) of the potassium chloride solution? Give your reasons.   H(2)

Total   15 marks

31 Solvation

The following table gives some data on lattice, solvation, and solution energies of some group I halides.

Halide	ΔH_{lat} /kJ mol^{-1}	ΔH_{solv} /kJ mol^{-1}	ΔH_{soln} /kJ mol^{-1}
LiCl	–	−958	+79
NaF	−918	–	+65
KF	−817	−770	+47
RbF	−784	−744	+40
CaF	−729	−711	+18

(a) How are the following defined:

   (i) solvation energy?   K (1)

   (ii) lattice energy?   K (1)

(b) The energy relationships principally involved in the dissolving of an ionic solid (ΔH_{lat}, ΔH_{soln}, ΔH_{solv}) may be represented by an energy cycle.

   (i) Draw to scale the cycle for lithium chloride.   C (2)

   (ii) Use the cycle to find a value for the lattice energy of lithium chloride.   C (2)

(c) The solvation energy for the ionic substance can be regarded as the sum of the solvation energies for its constituent ions. Calculate the solvation energy of sodium fluoride if the solvation energies of the sodium and fluoride ions are −390 and −457 kJ mol^{-1} respectively.   C (2)

(d) Explain why the solvation energy decreases on going down the group for a particular anion.   K (2)

(e) Name an organic solid which is soluble in water and give your reasons as to why it is soluble.   H (3)

(f) Consider the following physical properties of hydrogen fluoride:

        Melting point   = 190 K

        Dipole moment   = 6·38 × 10^{-30} C m (1.91 D)

        Relative permittivity = 175 (at 200 K)

Giving your reasons, state whether you think that liquid hydrogen fluoride is a suitable solvent for an ionic solid.   H (2)

Total   15 marks

32 Colligative properties

Colligative properties depend on the number of molecules or particles in the system rather than upon their nature. Two colligative properties such as the melting points and boiling points of solutions depend on variations in vapour pressures of these solutions. The following diagram shows the variation with temperature of the vapour pressure of a pure solvent (A) and the vapour pressure of a solution consisting of the solvent and some non-volatile undissociated or associated substance (B).

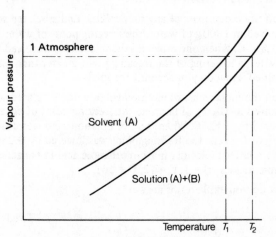

(a) Explain by a molecular picture why the solution of $[(A) + (B)]$ should have a lower vapour pressure than that of the pure solvent.   C(2)

(b) What do the quantities T_1 and T_2 represent?   C(1)

(c) (i) Explain, using a diagram of similar type to the one above, why addition of a non-volatile undissociated or associated substance to a pure solvent *lowers* the melting point of the pure solvent.   C(3)

  (ii) Describe what would happen if the liquid solution of $[(A) + (B)]$ was cooled slowly until the temperature was well below freezing point.   C(1)

 (iii) Describe what would happen if the liquid solution of $[(A) + (B)]$ was cooled *rapidly* below the freezing point.   K(1)

 (iv) Plot a temperature versus time graph for your answer to (c)(iii).   C(2)

(d) The following is a list of values for the enthalpies of fusion of the hydrides of group VI of the periodic table.

Hydride	H_2O	H_2S	H_2Se	H_2Te
Enthalpy of fusion /kJ mol^{-1}	6·02	2·38	2·50	4·18

    (i) What is meant by the term 'enthalpy of fusion'?   K(1)

   (ii) Explain why the enthalpy of fusion of water appears to be anomalous (compared with its analogues).   K(2)

(e) (i) Describe concisely what happens when concentrated enthanoic (acetic) acid is dissolved in water.   K(1)

   (ii) When the molar mass of any non-volatile undissociated solute is dissolved in 1000 g of water, the freezing point of water is lowered by 1.86 °C. When one mole of ethanoic acid is dissolved in 1000 g of water, a lowering of the freezing point greater than 1.86 °C is obtained. How do you account for this?   H(2)

  (iii) When the molar mass of any non-volatile undissociated solute is dissolved in 1000 g of benzene the freezing point of benzene is lowered by 5.12 °C. When 0.6 g of ethanoic acid was dissolved in 100 g of benzene the freezing point was lowered by 0.256 °C. What is the relative molecular mass of ethanoic acid in benzene (relative atomic masses: H = 1, C = 12, O = 16)?   H(2)

  (iv) How do you explain this answer?   H(2)

Total   20 marks

33 Vapour pressure and related phenomena

The curves in the figure below show the partial pressures and the total vapour pressure of various compositions of tetrachloromethane (carbon tetrachloride) and methanol (methyl alcohol) at 308 K.

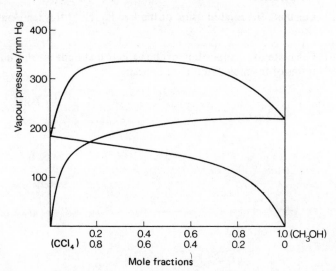

(a) (i) State Raoult's vapour pressure law.   K (2)

    (ii) How can Raoult's law be accounted for in terms of a molecular picture?   C (2)

    (iii) What type of deviation from Raoult's law is displayed in the above diagram?   C (1)

(b) Redraw the above diagram and include 'ideal' values, as dotted lines, of the partial pressures of the tetrachloromethane and methanol and the total vapour pressure of the mixture. Label all dotted lines.   C (2)

(c) (i) Explain briefly why the partial pressure of methanol over the mixture is greater than the ideal value.   C (2)

    (ii) Suggest two other liquids which together might show similar deviations.   K (1)

(d) Predict, giving your reasons, what temperature changes, if any, would occur if tetrachloromethane and methanol were mixed together.   H (2)

(e) Using a boiling point–composition diagram, explain why it is not possible to separate completely tetrachloromethane and methanol by fractional distillation.   C (3)

41

(f) A mixture of benzene and methylbenzene (toluene) behave as an ideal solution. When a solution of 0·66 moles of benzene and 0·34 moles of methylbenzene were boiled at one atmosphere pressure, the boiling point was 261 K. The vapour pressures of pure benzene and methylbenzene at this temperature are 955 and 380 mm respectively.

  (i) Calculate the partial pressures of the two liquids at the temperature.   C (2)

 (ii) Calculate the total pressure of the two liquids at this temperature.   C (1)

(iii) Calculate the composition of the vapour that boils off this liquid in terms of the mole fraction of benzene.   C (2)

Total   20 marks

34 Periodicity: second period*

The symbols of some elements are given below, but *not* in the correct order of increasing atomic number (3 to 10):

$$Li \quad B \quad Be \quad C \quad O \quad N \quad F \quad Ne$$

(a) Arrange the elements in order of increasing atomic number.　　　K(2)

(b) Write down the formulae of any four fluorides and state whether you think the fluoride you have quoted is a gas, liquid, or solid at room temperature.　　　C(4)

(c) Using 'dot-and-cross' notation, draw the structure of the fluoride of carbon.　　　H(2)

(d) Describe briefly how you could prepare any one fluoride in the laboratory.　　　H(2)

(e) (i) Name the oxides of three of these elements which would be classified as acidic.　　　C(3)

　　(ii) What molecular shape would you expect the oxide of fluorine (OF_2) to be? Give your reasons.　　　H(2)

(f) (i) Name two elements which may form ionic hydrides.　　　C(2)

　　(ii) Which elements form hydrides which show 'hydrogen bonding'?　C(3)

Total　20 marks

35 Periodicity: second period

The following information is concerned with the second period of elements of the periodic table.

	Li	Be	B	C	N	O	F	Ne
Atomic number	3	4	5	6	7	8	9	10
Covalent radius /pm	123	89	82	77	70	66	64	–
Ionic radius /pm	68	30	16	16	171	146	133	–
Electron affinity /kJ mol^{-1}	–57	–66	–15	–120	–31	–141	–332	–99
First ionization energy /kJ mol^{-1}	520	900	800	1086	1403	1314	1681	2081

(a) (i) Explain why hydrogen and helium are not placed in this period. C(2)

(ii) The values for hydrogen of the covalent radius, ionic radius (H$^-$), electron affinity and first ionization energy are 37 pm, 154 pm, –73 kJ mol^{-1}, and 1312 kJ mol^{-1} respectively. On the basis of this evidence, would you place hydrogen near lithium or fluorine? Give your reasons. H(2)

(b) (i) Explain why the ionic radii for the elements lithium to boron decrease. C(2)

(ii) Explain why the covalent radii decrease across the period. C(2)

(iii) Explain why the ionic radius of oxygen is larger than the covalent radius. C(2)

(c) How is the 'electron affinity' defined? K(1)

(d) (i) Why does beryllium have a high first ionization energy compared with lithium and boron? C(2)

(ii) Why does the ionization energy increase on going from carbon to neon? C(2)

Total   15 marks

36 Periodicity: problem

This question is concerned with element X of atomic number 37 and relative atomic mass 85·47. Use your knowledge of periodicity to answer the following questions.

(a) (i) What is the electronic configuration of X?   C(1)

    (ii) What is its principal oxidation number?   H(1)

(b) (i) Why is the relative atomic mass not a whole number, such as 85? C(1)

    (ii) How many protons does an atom of X contain?   C(1)

    (iii) How many neutrons might typical atoms of X contain? Give your reasons.   C(1)

(c) Is the element X a metal or a non-metal? Give your reasons.   C(1)

(d) (i) What is the formula of its stable oxide likely to be?   C(1)

    (ii) To what class of oxides does it belong (e.g. acidic, basic, etc.)?   C(1)

    (iii) What type of bonding would you expect in the oxide?   C(1)

(e) (i) What is the formula of the chloride likely to be?   C(1)

    (ii) How would this chloride be expected to react with water?   C(1)

    (iii) How would you prepare a small sample of this chloride?   C(2)

    (iv) Suggest how you could verify the formula of this chloride.   C(2)

Total   15 marks

37 Periodicity: third period*

The following table gives some information about certain elements in the third period of the periodic table.

	Sodium	Aluminium	Silicon	Sulphur	Chlorine
Atomic number	11	13	14	16	17
Melting point /K	371	932	1683	392	172
Electrical conductance	good	good	poor	poor	poor

(a) What are the symbols of the elements of atomic number 12 and 15?   K(2)

(b) The following information relates to one of the missing elements: melting point 923 K, density $1.74 \, g \, cm^{-3}$, electrical conductance good. State, giving reasons, whether you think the element has an atomic number of 12 or 15.   H(3)

(c) Use the following information about a chloride ($E_n Cl_m$) of one of the above elements to answer the questions.

The chloride of the element has a boiling point of 409 K; it does not conduct electricity in the liquid state. Aqueous solutions of the chloride do not exist because of hydrolysis. $200 \, cm^3$ of silver nitrate(V) (concentration $0.1 \, mol \, dm^{-3}$) are required to convert 0.01 mol of the chloride into silver chloride.

  (i) Is the chloride a liquid or gas at room temperature?   C(1)

  (ii) What is the value of m in the formula for the chloride?   H(2)

  (iii) On the basis of this formula, in which group of the periodic table would you place E?   C(1)

  (iv) Is this classification in accordance with the other data given? Give your reasons.   H(2)

  (v) If E is a member of group VI, what is the likely formula of the chloride?   C(1)

  (vi) What type of bonding would you expect in this chloride?   C(1)

  (vii) Write an equation for the hydrolysis of the chloride.   C(2)

Total   15 marks

38 Noble gas: xenon*

Xenon tetrafluoride, XeF_4, is a typical compound of the noble gases, and can be prepared by the action of fluorine on xenon for one hour at 673 K in a sealed container at about six atmospheres. Some xenon difluoride and hexafluoride are also formed so that purification is always necessary.

(a) The electronic configuration of xenon is (Kr) $4d^{10} 5s^2 5p^6$ (where Kr stands for the electronic configuration of krypton).

   (i) What is the number of bonding pairs of electrons in xenon tetrafluoride? C(1)

   (ii) What is the number of non-bonding pairs of electrons in xenon tetrafluoride? C(1)

   (iii) On what is the structure of xenon tetrafluoride based, e.g. pyramidal, octahedral, etc.? C(1)

   (iv) Draw a diagram to show the structure of xenon tetrafluoride. Include the bonding and the non-bonding pairs of electrons. H(2)

   (v) Would the xenon tetrafluoride molecule have a dipole moment? H(2)

(b) The enthalpy of the Xe—F bond in xenon tetrafluoride is 133 kJ mol^{-1}. Calculate the enthalpy change for the reaction

$$Xe\,(g) + 4F\,(g) \rightarrow XeF_4\,(g)$$ H(3)

(c) Water and xenon tetrafluoride react to form xenon trioxide, xenon and hydrogen fluoride. Write an equation for this reaction. C(2)

(d) In alkaline solutions xenon trioxide forms xenates according to the equation

$$2OH^-\,(aq) + 2XeO_3\,(s) \rightarrow 2HXeO_4^-\,(aq)$$

What is the oxidation state of xenon in this ion? C(1)

(e) Neon (atomic number 10) does not form a compound with fluorine. Can you suggest a reason for this? H(2)

Total   15 marks

39 Hydrogen and types of bonding*

Hydrogen atoms form three general types of compound, in which they occur as (1) cations, H^+, (2) anions, H^-, and (3) atoms participating in covalent bonding. Hydrogen atoms can also form unique bonds — the hydrogen bonds.

(a) How can H^+ cations be formed from covalent hydrides? C(2)

(b) Explain how H^+ cations can be used to form a covalent hydride. C(2)

(c) (i) Write down the formula of a compound containing the H^- anion. K(1)

    (ii) Describe briefly how this compound can be prepared. K(2)

    (iii) What is the reaction of water on this compound? Include an equation in your answer. C(2)

(d) In the series of hydrides H_2O, H_2S, H_2Se, H_2Te, the bond angle varies.

    (i) How does the bond angle vary? C(1)

    (ii) What is the cause of this variation? C(2)

(e) What is meant by the term 'hydrogen bond'? Use water molecules as an example. C(3)

(f) Explain why the melting point of 2-hydroxybenzaldehyde is much lower than 3- or 4-hydroxybenzaldehyde. H(2)

(g) Boron, a group III element, forms an unusual bond with hydrogen in B_2H_6 which may be called a 'three nucleus electron-pair bond'. Using 'dot-and-cross' notation, draw a diagram to show the structure of B_2H_6. H(3)

Total 20 marks

40 *s*-block: group I and II elements

The following table gives some information about group II elements.

	Beryllium	Magnesium	Calcium	Strontium	Barium
Atomic number	4	12	20	38	56
Ionic radius /pm	31	65	99	113	–
Density /g cm^{-3}	1.85	1·74	1·54	2·6	3·5
Abundance /p.p.m.	6	10 900	36 300	150	430

(a) Why are the elements listed not found native? K (2)

(b) (i) What is a possible source of magnesium in the earth's crust? K (1)

    (ii) How is any *one* of these elements obtained industrially? K (3)

(c) The ionic radii (in pm) of the group I elements are as follows:

Lithium	Sodium	Potassium	Rubidium	Caesium
68	98	133	148	169

    (i) What is meant by the term 'ionic radius'? K (2)

    (ii) The values of the ionic radii of the group I elements are larger than those for group II. How do you account for this? H (2)

    (iii) Explain why the ionic radius of sodium is approximately the same as that of calcium. H (2)

    (iv) Predict a value for the ionic radius of barium. C (1)

(d) The densities of beryllium, magnesium and calcium are lower than those for strontium and barium. Suggest a reason for this. H (2)

Total   15 marks

41 s-block: group I and II compounds

This question concerns the compounds of some s-block elements:
(A) $CaCO_3$, (B) $BaCl_2.xH_2O$, (C) NaI, (D) KNO_3, (E) $Ca(OH)_2$, (F) SrO,
(G) RbBr, (H) $MgSO_4.7H_2O$. Where applicable, use the letters denoting the compounds in your answer.

(a) Which substance(s) is/are ionic?   C(1)

(b) Which compound(s) contain(s) metals in group II of the periodic table?   C(5)

(c) Which compound(s) in solution would form a precipitate if added to silver nitrate(V) solution acidified with dilute nitric(V) acid?   C(3)

(d) Describe how substances E and H could be distinguished from each other.   C(2)

(e) Which substances do not dissolve to any great extent in water?   K(3)

(f)   (i) Give an equation for the action of heat on B.   C(1)

     (ii) Give an equation for the action of heat on D.   C(1)

(g) 3·05 g of B were dissolved in water to make $250\,cm^3$ of solution in a graduated flask. $20\,cm^3$ of this solution were reacted with 1 g of anhydrous sodium sulphate(VI) and the resulting solution was titrated with silver nitrate(V) solution (concentration $0·1\,mol\,dm^{-3}$) using potassium dichromate(VI) as indicator. It was found that $20\,cm^3$ were required. (Relative atomic masses: H = 1, O = 16, Cl = 35·5, Ba = 137.)

   (i) Why was the sodium sulphate(VI) added?   C(2)

   (ii) How many moles of silver ions were added during the titration?   C(1)

   (iii) How many moles of chloride ions were there in $20\,cm^3$ of the barium chloride solution?   C(1)

   (iv) How many moles of anhydrous barium chloride were there in $250\,cm^3$ of the solution?   C(1)

   (v) What is the relative molecular mass of the hydrated barium chloride?   C(2)

   (vi) What is the value of x in $BaCl_2.xH_2O$?   C(2)

Total   25 marks

42 Lattice energies of group II oxides

The lattice energy of calcium oxide is $-3523\,kJ\,mol^{-1}$. Study the information listed below and then answer the questions.

(A)   The enthalpy of atomization of calcium = $176\,kJ\,mol^{-1}$
(B)   The third ionization energy of calcium = $4900\,kJ\,mol^{-1}$
(C)   The enthalpy of atomization of oxygen = $250\,kJ\,mol^{-1}$
(D)   The second ionization energy of oxygen = $3499\,kJ\,mol^{-1}$
(E)   The second ionization energy of calcium = $1100\,kJ\,mol^{-1}$
(F)   The electrode potential $Ca^{2+}(aq)/Ca(s) = -2.87\,V$
(G)   The enthalpy of formation of $CaO(s) = -635\,kJ\,mol^{-1}$
(H)   The first ionization energy of calcium = $590\,kJ\,mol^{-1}$
(I)   The first ionization energy of oxygen = $1310\,kJ\,mol^{-1}$

(a)   (i)   Define the lattice energy of calcium oxide.   K (1)

      (ii)   Define the electron affinity of oxygen.   K (1)

(b)   (i)   In addition to the lattice energy of calcium oxide, which of the processes listed above, A to I, would be required in order to determine the total electron affinity of oxygen. Use the letters A to I in your answer.   H (2)

      (ii)   Calculate a value for the total electron affinity of oxygen.   C (4)

(c)   (i)   Why is the third ionization energy of calcium much larger than the the first or second?   C (2)

      (ii)   Why is the first ionization energy of oxygen larger than that for calcium?   C (2)

(d)   The lattice energies of some of the oxides of group II elements are given below.

Oxide	Lattice energy /kJ mol⁻¹
Beryllium oxide	-4519
Magnesium oxide	-3933
Calcium oxide	-3523
Strontium oxide	-3310

      (i)   Why does the value of the lattice energy decrease on descending the group?   C (2)

      (ii)   Would you expect the lattice energies of the group I oxides to be higher or lower? Give your reasons.   H (2)

(e) (i) Suggest why the group II oxides might be used as refractories. H(2)

(ii) Which oxide would you expect to be the best refractory? Give your reasons. H(2)

Total   20 marks

43 *s*-block: sodium carbonate manufacture

The raw materials for the manufacture of sodium carbonate, by the Solvay process, are calcium carbonate and sodium chloride. These substances do not give sodium carbonate directly and the process depends upon the fact that sodium hydrogencarbonate is insoluble in brine saturated with ammonia and carbon dioxide.

(a) What is the purpose of the calcium carbonate?   C(2)

(b) The first stage of manufacture is the ammoniation of brine.

   (i) How is this achieved?   C(2)

   (ii) What is the source of ammonia?   K(1)

(c) The second stage can be regarded as the carbonation of the ammoniated brine.

   (i) What is meant by the term 'carbonation'?   K(2)

   (ii) Write two equations to show what happens at this stage.   C(2)

(d) The final stage is the conversion of sodium hydrogencarbonate to sodium carbonate. How is this achieved?   C(2)

(e) What is the maximum mass of sodium carbonate that could be obtained from 117 kg of sodium chloride? (Relative atomic masses: C = 12, O = 16, Na = 23, Cl = 35.5.)   C(4)

(f) Suggest what would happen if the anhydrous sodium carbonate obtained were exposed to the atmosphere for several days.   C(1)

(g) The process of the production of sodium carbonate is very economical. Suggest why this is so.   H(2)

(h) Explain why the Solvay process cannot be applied to the manufacture of potassium carbonate.   H(2)

Total   20 marks

44 *s*-block: group II compounds*

The elements of group II form a number of insoluble compounds. The following table gives values for the solubility products of some of these compounds.

Compound	Solubility product (K_{sp})
Beryllium hydroxide, $Be(OH)_2$	2.0×10^{-18} mol^3 dm^{-9}
Magnesium hydroxide, $Mg(OH)_2$	2.0×10^{-11} mol^3 dm^{-9}
Calcium sulphate(VI), $CaSO_4$	2.0×10^{-5} mol^2 dm^{-6}
Strontium carbonate, $SrCO_3$	1.1×10^{-10} mol^2 dm^{-6}
Barium carbonate, $BaCO_3$	5.5×10^{-10} mol^2 dm^{-6}

(a) (i) Which is the least soluble hydroxide?   C(1)

    (ii) Which carbonate is the most soluble?   C(1)

(b) (i) What type of bonding occurs in magnesium hydroxide?   K(1)

    (ii) Draw a 'dot-and-cross' diagram to illustrate this bonding.   C(2)

(c) (i) Calculate the solubility of beryllium hydroxide in mol dm^{-3}.   H(3)

    (ii) Calculate the pH of a saturated solution of beryllium hydroxide. H(3)

(d) How would you detect experimentally the presence of

    (i) barium cations in a saturated solution of barium carbonate?   H(1)

    (ii) sulphate(VI) anions in a saturated solution of calcium sulphate(VI)?   H(1)

(e) What do you think would happen if equal volumes of saturated solutions of beryllium hydroxide and magnesium hydroxide were mixed together?   H(2)

Total   15 marks

45 Group III: elements

The following table shows the atomic numbers of elements in group III, together with the ionic radii and the electrode potentials.

	Boron	Aluminium	Gallium	Indium
Atomic number	5	13	31	49
Ionic radius /pm	16	45	62	81
Electrode potential M^{3+} (aq)/M(s)/V	–	−1·66	−0·53	−0·34

(a) Write down the electronic configuration of the

   (i) aluminium atom.   C(1)

   (ii) aluminium ion.   C(1)

(b) Account for the increase in ionic radius in the group: boron, aluminium, gallium, indium.   C(2)

(c) The properties of boron can be summarized in the following way: covalent polymer, very hard, black metallic appearance, semi-conductor, high melting point, inert to acids, steam and air. Using the same type of terminology describe the properties of aluminium.   H(3)

(d) Refer to the electrode potentials given above.

   (i) Which metal is the best reducing agent?   C(1)

   (ii) Which ion is the best oxidizing agent?   C(1)

   (iii) Will aluminium metal react with indium ions to produce indium metal?   H(2)

   (iv) Will aluminium ions react with gallium metal to produce aluminium metal?   H(2)

(e) The electrode potential of boron is not quoted because of the total absence of the cation B^{3+}. How do you account for the absence of this cation? H(2)

Total   15 marks

46 Group III: manufacture of aluminium

Read the following passage† and then answer the questions below.

In ALCOA's new process, alumina (aluminium oxide, Al_2O_3), refined from bauxite ore, is combined with chlorine in a reactor unit. This converts the oxide to aluminium chloride, $AlCl_3$. The chloride is then processed electrolytically in a closed cell which separates the compound into molten aluminium and chlorine.

The traditional process for extracting aluminium from bauxite is also electrolytic. In this case, however, the alumina is dissolved in molten cryolite [sodium hexafluoroaluminate(III)]. According to ALCOA, cryolite is becoming increasingly scarce and expensive. It also causes the production of fluoride emissions, so that the aluminium smelter designers have to spend a lot of money on systems for containing these dangerous chemicals.

(a) How is aluminium oxide obtained from bauxite ore?   C(4)

(b) Write an equation for the reaction between alumina and chlorine.   C(2)

(c) What do you understand by the phrase 'processed electrolytically'?   C(2)

(d) What is the function of cryolite in the traditional process?   K(2)

(e) How many moles of electrons are required to liberate one mole of aluminium atoms from

    (i)   aluminium chloride?   C(1)

    (ii) aluminium oxide?   C(1)

(f) On the basis of your answers in (e) only, will the new process be more economical than the traditional? Give your reasons.   H(3)

Total   15 marks

---

†Adapted from *New Scientist,* 1 March 1973, p 487

47 Group III: aluminium chloride*

It is found that as the melting point of aluminium chloride is approached the electrical conductance increases rapidly and then at the melting point falls suddenly to nearly zero. The relative density of the vapour at a temperature just before the melting point is 66·7. At temperatures greater than the melting point it is 133·5. Further heating of the vapour produces a decrease in the relative density.

Relative atomic masses: Al = 27, Cl = 35·5

(a) What is the relative molecular mass of aluminium chloride in the vapour state

    (i) just before the melting point?   C(1)

    (ii) just after the melting point?   C(1)

(b) What are the formulae of aluminium chloride corresponding to these relative molecular masses?   H(2)

(c) Account for the rise in conductance as the melting point is approached.   H(2)

(d) Why does the electrical conductance decrease at the melting point?   H(2)

(e) (i) Suggest a structure for the aluminium chloride at temperatures greater than the melting point.   H(2)

    (ii) Would the substance of this structure be soluble in tetrachloromethane (carbon tetrachloride)? Give your reasons.   H(3)

(f) Suggest why further heating of the aluminium chloride vapour produces a decrease in the relative density.   H(2)

Total   15 marks

48 Group IV: elements

The following table gives some information about the elements in group IV.

	Carbon (diamond)	Silicon	Germanium	Tin	Lead
Ionic radius E^{2+}/pm	–	–	93	112	120
Enthalpy of vaporization /kJ mol^{-1}	718	297	285	291	178
Bond enthalpy $E-E$ /kJ mol^{-1}	347	226	185	150	272

(a) (i) Why are there no values given for the ionic radii of C^{2+} and Si^{2+}? C(2)

    (ii) Why do the values of the ionic radii increase in going from germanium to lead? C(2)

(b) (i) Why is the enthalpy of vaporization of diamond much higher than that of silicon despite their similar structure? H(2)

    (ii) Suggest two other properties which might show the same effect. H(2)

(c) The element germanium is often referred to as a semi-metal.

    (i) What does the term 'semi-metal' mean? K(2)

    (ii) Suggest a physical property that would provide information that germanium is a semi-metal. H(1)

    (iii) To what use are semi-metals put? K(2)

(d) Catenation (the ability of atoms to bond directly to atoms of the same element to form chains or rings) is much greater in carbon than for other elements in group IV. Explain why this is so. H(2)

Total 15 marks

49 Group IV: tin(II) chloride

The following questions are concerned with the preparation and properties of tin(II) chloride.

(a) (i) Tin(II) chloride can be prepared by passing dry hydrogen chloride over heated tin in a suitable apparatus. Draw a diagram to illustrate the preparation.   C(3)

   (ii) Explain why hydrogen chloride is used in preference to chlorine C(2)

  (iii) The product obtained should be white, but is often discoloured. Suggest a reason for this.   H(2)

(b) Tin(II) chloride is found to be soluble in organic solvents. What does this tell you about the bonding in tin(II) chloride?   H(2)

(c) Explain why gaseous tin(II) chloride is an angular molecule rather than a linear one.   H(2)

(d) If a concentrated solution of tin(II) chloride is diluted, a white precipitate is produced. Suggest a reason for this.   C(2)

(e) On addition of alkali to a tin(II) chloride solution a white precipitate is observed which dissolves on further addition of alkali. Write two equations to show the chemical reactions taking place.   H(4)

(f) Using the data below, suggest what would happen if a solution of tin(II) chloride were added to cerium(IV) sulphate solution.

$$E^\ominus \; Sn^{4+}(aq)/Sn^{2+}(aq) \; = +0.15 \, V$$
$$E^\ominus \; Sn^{2+}(aq)/Sn(s) \quad\; = -0.14 \, V$$
$$E^\ominus \; Ce^{4+}(aq)/Ce^{3+}(aq) \; = +1.70 \, V$$
$$E^\ominus \; Ce^{3+}(aq)/Ce(s) \quad\; = -2.33 \, V$$

H(3)

Total   20 marks

50 Group IV: oxides

The following is a short statement about the oxides of the elements in group IV. Read it carefully and then answer the questions.

All the following oxides (CO_2, SiO_2, GeO_2, SnO_2) can be prepared by the direct combination of the element and oxygen. Lead(IV) oxide cannot be prepared in this way. Carbon dioxide in all three states of matter is composed of discrete molecules. The other oxides are network lattices involving bonds of varying degrees of polarity. Silicon(IV) oxide (quartz) has a melting point of 1983 K, and germanium and tin oxides similarly have high melting points.

(a) Suggest why lead(IV) oxide cannot be prepared by the general method.
H(2)

(b) Solid carbon dioxide sublimes at 194 K at one atmosphere pressure.

  (i) What does this statement mean?   C(2)

  (ii) What forces hold the molecules together in the solid state?   K(1)

(c) (i) What do you understand by the term 'polarity'?   K(2)

  (ii) In what way do you think the polarity of the oxides will vary down the group?   H(2)

(d) Why are the melting points of silicon(IV) oxide, germanium(IV) oxide, tin(IV) oxide, and lead(IV) oxide much higher than that of carbon dioxide?   C(2)

(e) Oxides may be classified into acidic, basic, amphoteric, and neutral according to how they behave with acids, alkalis, and water.

  (i) Classify the oxides of the elements in group IV in this way.   C(3)

  (ii) Account for this trend.   H(2)

(f) (i) When a microscope slide is dropped into a beaker containing hydrofluoric acid, the slide becomes opaque. Explain the observation. Give an equation for the chemical reaction taking place.   H(3)

  (ii) To what use is this reaction put in the glass industry?   K(1)

Total   20 marks

51 Group V: hydrides

The following table shows the atomic numbers of the elements in group V of the periodic table and the boiling points of their hydrides.

	Nitrogen	Phosphorus	Arsenic	Antimony	Bismuth
Atomic number	7	15	33	51	83
Boiling point of hydride /K	240	186	211	256	251

(a) What is the general formula of the hydrides?   K (1)

(b) What type of chemical bonding is encountered in the pure hydrides?   K (1)

(c)   (i)   Explain briefly why the boiling points of the hydrides increase in the group phosphorus, arsenic, antimony, and bismuth.   H (2)

   (ii)   Explain why the nitrogen hydride has a relatively high boiling point.   C (2)

   (iii)   Suggest two other physical properties which might show a similar effect.   H (2)

(d) Give balanced equations describing the reactions between

   (i)   the nitrogen hydride and water.   C (1)

   (ii)   the nitrogen hydride and hydrogen chloride.   C (1)

(e) The nitrogen hydride can be liquefied either by cooling the gas at atmospheric pressure or by compression to nine atmospheres at room temperature.

   (i)   Why do both these operations produce the liquid hydride?   H (2)

   (ii)   What ionic species are likely to be present in the liquid hydride?   H (2)

   (iii)   Would the liquid hydride be acidic, alkaline, or neutral?   H (1)

Total   15 marks

52 'The great red spot of Jupiter'

It has been claimed (*Science,* 17 October 1975) that the red spot of Jupiter is caused by small particles of red phosphorus.

Phosphine, PH_3, is present in the outer 'atmosphere' of Jupiter to the extent of four molecules per ten million. Among the other molecules, molecular hydrogen and helium are in the majority. Irradiation of the phosphine molecules by ultraviolet light from the sun produces unstable PH_2 molecules. These PH_2 molecules react with themselves to produce white molecular phosphorus, P_4, and hydrogen. When physical conditions such as temperature and pressure permit, the molecules of phosphorus react to form crystals of red phosphorus − the red spot.

In the region of the red spot there is a relatively rapid mixing between different layers in the atmosphere. The red phosphorus crystals, once formed, fall quickly in the atmosphere until they reach a temperature where they evaporate. Here the P_4 molecules again react with hydrogen to give phosphine; this then rises to the outer atmosphere.

(a) If a mole of particles was taken from the outer atmosphere of Jupiter, how many phosphine molecules would be present ($L = 6 \cdot 0 \times 10^{23}$)? C(1)

(b) What is the difference between molecular hydrogen and atomic hydrogen? K(1)

(c) Write an equation to show how molecular phosphorus is formed from unstable PH_2 molecules. C(1)

(d) (i) Draw a 'dot-and-cross' diagram to show the bonding in PH_2. H(2)

    (ii) If the HPH bond angle in phosphine is $94°$, predict what the bond angle might be in PH_2. Give your reasons. H(2)

(e) Show by means of a diagram that phosphorus undergoes a cycle in the atmosphere of Jupiter. C(2)

(f) The standard enthalpy of formation of phosphine is $+9 \cdot 25$ kJ mol^{-1}. What does this information tell you about the stability of this compound with respect to its constituent elements? C(2)

(g) Like ammonia, phosphine can produce ions of the type XH_4^+ (e.g. $PH_4^+I^-$).

    (i) Predict what shape the PH_4^+ ion would adopt. H(1)

    (ii) Write an equation to show how the salt $PH_4^+I^-$ could be prepared, given that it is completely hydrolyzed in water. H(2)

    (iii) If the salt were added to water, what might the resulting pH of the solution be? H(1)

Total 15 marks

53 Group V: nitrates

Study the following reaction scheme and then answer the questions below.

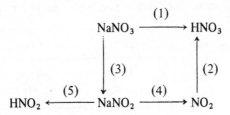

(a) In which of the five compounds listed does nitrogen have the highest oxidation state?   C (2)

(b) Describe how stage (1) may be achieved in the laboratory.   K (2)

(c) In industry, nitric(V) acid is obtained from ammonia by oxidation to nitrogen oxide. This in turn is oxidized by air to nitrogen dioxide. Finally, the resulting gas is then passed into water to yield nitric(V) acid and nitrogen oxide (stage 2). Complete the following equations to illustrate the process.

  (i) $NH_3(g) + O_2(g) \longrightarrow$ C (1)

  (ii) $NO(g) + O_2(g) \longrightarrow$ C (1)

  (iii) $NO_2(g) + H_2O(l) \longrightarrow$ C (1)

(d) When sodium nitrate(V) is heated sodium nitrate(III) is produced (stage 3).

  (i)   What other product is obtained in this reaction?   C (1)

  (ii)   How could this product be identified?   K (1)

(e) How can stage (4) be achieved?   K (2)

(f) Nitric(III) (nitrous) acid is a weak acid ($K_a = 4 \cdot 7 \times 10^{-4} \text{ mol dm}^{-3}$) and is unstable in the pure state. How can stage (5) be achieved in the laboratory?   K (2)

(g) The decomposition of the pure acid can be represented by the redox equation

$$3HNO_2(l) \longrightarrow H^+(aq) + NO_3^-(aq) + 2NO(g) + H_2O(l)$$

  (i)   Which species is the oxidant?   C (1)

  (ii)   Which species is the reductant?   C (1)

  (iii)   Calculate the pH of a solution of the acid (concentration $0 \cdot 001$ mol dm^{-3}).   C (3)

  (iv)   Suggest briefly a possible way in which the rate of decomposition of the acid could be measured at room temperature.   H (2)

Total   20 marks

54 Group VI: elements

The following table shows the atomic numbers of elements in group VI of the periodic table and the common oxidation numbers of each element.

	Oxygen	Sulphur	Selenium	Tellurium
Atomic number	8	16	34	52
Oxidation numbers	$-2, -1$	$-2, +2, +4, +6$	$-2, +2, +4, +6,$	$+2, +4, +6$

(a) Give the electronic configuration of

   (i) oxygen.   C(1)

   (ii) sulphur.   C(1)

(b) Give the electronic configuration that could be ascribed to sulphur in oxidation state

   (i) -2.   C(1)

   (ii) $+2$.   C(1)

(c) Give the formula of a compound of sulphur when the oxidation state of sulphur is

   (i) -2.   H(1)

   (ii) $+2$.   H(1)

   (iii) $+4$.   H(1)

(d) Polonium is the last member of group VI. What two oxidation states are most likely to be found in its compounds?   H(2)

(e) Both tellurium and sulphur form fluorides where the oxidation state of the elements is +6.

   (i) State the formulae of these fluorides.   C(2)

   (ii) The tellurium fluoride is rapidly hydrolyzed by water to telluric acid, $Te(OH)_6$, and hydrofluoric acid. Write an equation for this reaction.   C(2)

   (iii) Sulphur hexafluoride is stable, even by boiling alkali. Comment on the difference between this and tellurium hexafluoride.   H(2)

Total   15 marks

55 Group VI: preparation of sodium thiosulphate(VI)

Read the following passage and then answer the questions.

To prepare sodium thiosulphate ($Na_2S_2O_3.5H_2O$) put 16 g of hydrated sodium sulphite ($Na_2SO_3.7H_2O$), 4 g of flowers of sulphur and 12 cm^3 of water in a 100 cm^3 round-bottomed flask. Fit a reflux condenser to the flask and reflux for 60 minutes or until all the sodium sulphite (Na_2SO_3) has dissolved. Filter off the excess sulphur and wash it with a small volume of water (4–6 cm^3). The filtrate should be evaporated until the volume is reduced to about 12 cm^3. Allow the solution to crystallize by standing the beaker in a bath of cold water. When crystallization is complete, filter through a Hirsch funnel and dry the crystals obtained with filter paper. The yield should be about 8 g.

(a) What is the oxidation state of sulphur in

    (i) sodium sulphite?   C (1)

    (ii) elemental sulphur?   C (1)

(b) (i) What is the purpose of the reflux condenser?   C (2)

    (ii) Why does the filtrate have to be evaporated?   C (1)

    (iii) Why is the beaker placed in a bath of cold water?   C (1)

    (iv) What is the advantage of using a Hirsch funnel compared with an ordinary funnel?   C (1)

(c) Write an ionic equation for preparation of the sodium thiosulphate.   H (2)

(d) Calculate the theoretical yield of hydrated sodium thiosulphate.

    (Relative atomic masses: H = 1, O = 16, Na = 23, S = 32.)   H (3)

(e) How do you account for the difference between the theoretical and the actual yield?   H (2)

(f) (i) In analyzing the crystals to determine the percentage purity, 2·5 g of the sodium thiosulphate crystals were made up to 100 cm^3 of solution. Unfortunately, the flask had not been washed and contained traces of acid. After a few minutes the solution went cloudy. Suggest an explanation for this cloudiness. Include an equation in your answer.   H (3)

    (ii) A new portion of sodium thiosulphate was made up in order to determine the percentage purity. Describe briefly how this could be achieved.   H (3)

Total   20 marks

56 Group VI: sulphuric(VI) acid

The following reaction scheme (1) – (7) is concerned with the industrial manufacture of sulphuric(VI) acid. Study the scheme carefully and then answer the
questions.

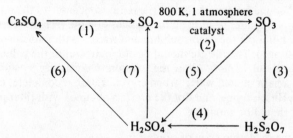

(a) (i) With what substances is the calcium sulphate(VI) heated in (1)? K (1)

    (ii) What could be used as an alternative source of sulphur dioxide? K (2)

(b) Conversion (2) involves the catalytic oxidation of sulphur dioxide to
sulphur(VI) oxide (sulphur trioxide).

    (i) What is the catalyst used? K (1)

    (ii) Explain why a temperature of 800 K is used instead of, say,
1200 K. C (2)

    (iii) Explain why the process is not favoured by low pressure. C (2)

(c) (i) How is conversion (3) obtained? K (2)

    (ii) What is the name of the product? K (1)

    (iii) What is the oxidation state of sulphur in $H_2S_2O_7$? C (1)

(d) (i) How is conversion (4) obtained? K (2)

    (ii) Why is conversion (5) not normally done in industry? H (2)

(e) Write equations to show how the following could be
accomplished:

    (i) conversion (6). C (2)

    (ii) conversion (7). C (2)

Total 20 marks

57 Group VII: elements

The following table gives some information about elements in group VII of the periodic table.

	Fluorine	Chlorine	Bromine	Iodine
Atomic number	9	17	35	53
Dissociation energy /kJ mol^{-1}	79	122	96	76
Hydration energy of gaseous ions /kJ mol^{-1}	560	385	351	305
Enthalpy of vaporization /kJ mol^{-1}	3.3	10·2	15	30

(a) What is meant by the term

   (i) 'dissociation energy'?   K (2)

   (ii) 'hydration energy'?   K (2)

(b) Account for the increase in enthalpy of vaporization down the group. C (2)

(c) (i) Comment on the low value for the dissociation energy and high value for the hydration energy of fluorine.   H (2)

   (ii) To what physical property of fluorine do these values contribute?   C (1)

(d) If the electron affinity of bromine is $340 \, kJ \, mol^{-1}$, calculate the value of the enthalpy change for the reaction

$$\tfrac{1}{2} Br_2(g) \longrightarrow Br^-(aq) \qquad\qquad H (3)$$

(e) Chlorine is often prepared by the action of hot concentrated hydrochloric acid on manganese(IV) oxide. Is this in accordance with the following data? If not, why not?

   $[MnO_2 \, (s) + 4H^+ \, (aq)], \, [Mn^{2+} \, (aq) + 2H_2O(l)]/Pt \;\; E^{\ominus} = +1·23 \, V$

   $Cl_2 \, (aq), \, 2Cl^- \, (aq)/Pt \qquad\qquad\qquad\qquad E^{\ominus} = +1·36 \, V$ H (3)

Total   15 marks

58 Group VII: hydrides*

The hydrides of group VII are pungent, colourless gases at room temperature. They fume in moist air and are soluble in water.

(a) The hydrogen fluoride and chloride are usually prepared by the action of concentrated sulphuric(VI) acid on the corresponding sodium salt.

   (i) Write an equation to show how hydrogen fluoride can be prepared in this way.   C(1)

   (ii) Explain why hydrogen bromide and iodide cannot be prepared by this method.   C(2)

   (iii) How can hydrogen bromide be prepared?   K(2)

(b) The boiling points (K) of the hydrides are given below.

Hydride	Boiling point/K
Hydrogen fluoride	253
Hydrogen chloride	188
Hydrogen bromide	206
Hydrogen iodide	238

How do you account for the anomalous value for hydrogen fluoride?   H(2)

(c) In water, hydrogen fluoride behaves as a weak acid and all the others are strong acids, but in some solvents, such as methanoic acid, the order of increasing acid strength is HF < HCl < HBr < HI. Account for this.   H(2)

(d) Hydrogen iodide is the only one of these gases to undergo any significant thermal dissociation at 1300 K. At this temperature the dissociation is 20 per cent.

   (i) Write an equation for the dissociation.   C(1)

   (ii) Write down an expression for the equilibrium constant K_p in terms of α, the degree of dissociation, and P, the total pressure.   H(3)

   (iii) Calculate the value of K_p at 1300 K and a total pressure of one atmosphere.   C(2)

Total   15 marks

59 Group VII: oxides and oxoacids of chlorine*

The following table shows the oxides and oxoacids of chlorine together with the ionization constants of the acids.

Oxide	Oxoacid	K_a /mol dm^{-3}
$Cl_2O(g)$	HOCl	3.7×10^{-8}
–	$HClO_2$	1.0×10^{-2}
$ClO_2(g)$	$HClO_3$	10
$Cl_2O_6(l)$	–	–
$Cl_2O_7(l)$	$HClO_4$	10^{10}

(a) What is the oxidation state of chlorine in

   (i) ClO?   C (1)

   (ii) Cl_2O_7?   C (1)

(b) Using 'dot-and-cross' notation, draw a diagram to show the bonding in Cl_2O.   C (2)

(c) Dichlorine hexaoxide, Cl_2O_6, is prepared by treating trioxygen (ozone) with chlorine dioxide. Write an equation to show this reaction.   C (2)

(d) Which of the two oxides Cl_2O_6 or Cl_2O_7 would you expect to have the higher boiling point? Give your reasons.   H (2)

(e) (i) Which of the acids listed is the strongest?   C (1)

   (ii) Draw the structural formula of the acid $HClO_3$.   H (2)

   (iii) Calculate the pK_a for the acid HOCl.   C (2)

   (iv) Why do you think the values given for $HClO_3$ and $HClO_4$ are only approximate?   H (2)

Total   15 marks

60 Transition elements

Study the graphs below and then answer the questions.

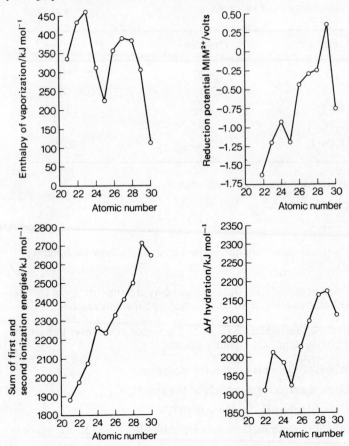

(a) (i) Comment on the similar shape of all the graphs, i.e. 'the double hump'. Explain why there is a minimum at atomic number 25.   H(3)

   (ii) Suggest another property which might show a similar shape.   H(1)

   (iii) What is the electronic configuration of element atomic number 25?   C(1)

(b) (i) What is the atomic number of the element with the greatest oxidizing power?   C(1)

   (ii) What is the atomic number of the element with the greatest reducing power?   C(1)

(iii) In terms of what electrode are these reduction potentials
quoted?   K(1)

(c) (i) How is the enthalpy of vaporization defined?   K(2)

(ii) Describe briefly how the enthalpy of vaporization can be determined
for a simple liquid.   C(2)

(d) The standard potentials $E^{\ominus}$ are related to the standard free energy change
for the reaction

$$M^{2+}(aq) + H_2(g) \rightleftharpoons M(s) + 2H^+(aq)$$

The enthalpy change $\Delta H^{\ominus}$ for the reaction can be obtained from

$$\Delta H^{\ominus} = \Delta H_a + \Delta H_1 + \Delta H_2 + \Delta H(H^+) + \Delta H_h$$

where ΔH_a is the enthalpy of atomization, $\Delta H(H^+)$ relates to the reaction

$$(2H^+(aq) + 2e^- \rightleftharpoons H_2(g) + aq \; (\Delta H(H^+) = -810 \, kJ \, mol^{-1})$$

ΔH_h is the enthalpy of hydration, and ΔH_1 and ΔH_2 are the first and
second ionization energies respectively. Draw an energy cycle for element
atomic number 25 to determine $\Delta H^{\ominus}$. Use the graphs and assume
$\Delta H_a = 530 \, kJ \, mol^{-1}$.   H(3)

Total   15 marks

61 Titanium

Titanium (Ti) is a typical transition element. Its atomic number is 22.

(a) (i)   What is the electronic configuration of titanium?   C (1)

 (ii) What are the principal oxidation states of titanium likely to be? H (2)

 (iii) List four typical properties you would expect titanium to have. K (4)

(b) The chloride, $TiCl_4$, can be prepared in the laboratory by passing chlorine
over a hot mixture of titanium(IV) oxide and carbon. It is a colourless
liquid having a melting point of 250 K.

 (i)   Write an equation to show the preparation of the chloride.   C (1)

 (ii) What type of bonding would you expect in this chloride? Give your
reasons.   H (2)

 (iii) Titanium does not form an ion $[Ti(H_2O)_4]^{4+}$ in aqueous solution.
Suggest a reason for this.   H (2)

 (iv) Acid solutions of titanium(IV) ions react quantitatively with hydrogen
peroxide to yield a brilliant orange-coloured species, TiO_2^{2+} (aq).
If you were given a solution of hydrogen peroxide of unknown
concentration, a solution of known concentration, and some
acidified titanium(IV) solution, describe how you would determine
the concentration of the unknown hydrogen peroxide solution. H (3)

(c) When 3 g of titanium(IV) chloride were completely reacted with zinc and
hydrochloric acid, the solution turned a purple colour. This solution was
then made up to $250 \, cm^3$ with water. It was found that $25 \, cm^3$ of the
solution reacted with $25 \, cm^3$ of an iron(III) chloride solution (concentration $0 \cdot 1 \, mol \, dm^{-3}$). Relative atomic masses are $Cl = 35.5$ and $Ti = 48$.

 (i)   How many moles are there present in 3 g of titanium(IV)
chloride?   C (1)

 (ii) What is the concentration (in $mol \, dm^{-3}$) of the solution when it is
made up to $250 \, cm^3$?   C (1)

 (iii) What is the oxidation state of titanium after the titanium(IV)
chloride has reacted with zinc and hydrochloric acid? Give your
reasons.   H (2)

 (iv) Write an ionic equation for the reaction between iron(III) ions and
the titanium ion produced after reaction with zinc and hydrochloric
acid.   C (1)

Total   20 marks

62 Vanadium*

The atomic number of vanadium is 23.

(a) (i) Why is vanadium classified as a transition element? K(1)

   (ii) What is the electronic configuration of vanadium? C(1)

(b) Vanadium forms a number of oxides in which the oxidation numbers are +2, +3, +4, and +5.

   (i) Give the formulae of the oxides corresponding to these oxidation states. C(2)

   (ii) What is the electronic configuration of vanadium in the oxidation state +2 and in the oxidation state +5? C(2)

(c) The ionic radii of both V^{2+} and Ca^{2+} are approximately 90 pm, yet their chemistry is very different. Explain why this is so. H(3)

(d) Look at the following reduction potentials (referring to half-cells).

$$VO_2^+ (aq) + 2H^+ (aq) + e^- \rightarrow VO^{2+} (aq) + H_2O(l) \quad E^\ominus = 1 \cdot 0 \, V$$
$$VO^{2+} (aq) + 2H^+ (aq) + 5H_2O(l) + e^- \rightarrow [V(H_2O)_6]^{3+} \quad E^\ominus = 0 \cdot 36 \, V$$
$$[V(H_2O)_6]^{3+} (aq) + e^- \rightarrow [V(H_2O)_6]^{2+} (aq) \quad E^\ominus = 0 \cdot 25 \, V$$

   (i) What is the oxidation number of vanadium in the ion VO_2^+? C(1)

   (ii) Which ion is the strongest reducing agent? C(1)

   (iii) Predict what would happen if a solution containing $[V(H_2O)_6]^{2+}$ ions were mixed with a solution containing VO_2^+ ions? H(2)

   (iv) Predict what would happen if a piece of magnesium was dipped into a solution containing $[V(H_2O)_6]^{2+}$ ions. H(2)

$$Mg^{2+} (aq) + 2e^- \rightarrow Mg(s) \quad E^\ominus = -2 \cdot 37 \, V$$

   (v) State, giving your reasons, whether you would expect an acidic solution of $[V(H_2O)_6]^{2+}$ ions to oxidize hydrogen peroxide to oxygen?

$$H_2O_2 (aq) \rightarrow O_2 (g) + 2H^+ (aq) + 2e^- \quad E^\ominus = 0 \cdot 7 \, V \quad H(2)$$

(e) Account for the following trend in the ionization energies of vanadium.

	First	Second	Third	Fourth	Fifth	Sixth
Ionization energy /kJ mol^{-1}	650	1414	2866	4632	6793	12 435

H(3)

Total 20 marks

63 Potassium chromate(VI)*

When crystalline potassium chromate(VI) was dissolved in water, a yellow solution A was formed. The addition of dilute sulphuric(VI) acid to A gave an orange solution B. When hydrogen sulphide was bubbled through solution B, the solution changed colour and gave a solution C, with a yellow precipitate. The yellow precipitate was filtered off. When ammonium chloride and aqueous ammonia were added to the filtrate, a green gelatinous precipitate D was obtained. Upon the addition of hydrogen peroxide to D the precipitate dissolved and a clear yellow solution resulted.

(a) (i) Write down the formulae of the species containing chromium in each of A, B, C, and D.   H(4)

    (ii) In which of these compounds has the chromium the highest oxidation state?   C(2)

(b) How are the ligands arranged around the chromium in C?   H(1)

(c) How do you account for the change in colour when dilute sulphuric acid was added to A? Give an equation in your answer.   C(2)

(d) (i) What is the yellow substance obtained after passing hydrogen sulphide through B?   C(1)

    (ii) Give an equation for the reaction taking place between hydrogen sulphide and B.   C(1)

(e) Why were ammonium chloride and aqueous ammonia added and not, say, dilute sodium hydroxide?   H(2)

(f) (i) What was the yellow solution obtained when hydrogen peroxide was added to D?   C(1)

    (ii) To what class of reaction would this belong?   K(1)

Total   15 marks

64 Manganese(IV) oxide*

If manganese(IV) oxide were slowly added to a heated mixture of potassium hydroxide and potassium chlorate(V) in an iron crucible, a melt would be obtained which, when cooled and then shaken with water, would produce a green solution A. If A is acidified, a dark-coloured solution B is obtained which, when filtered, produces a purple solution containing substance C.

(a) What is the function of the potassium chlorate(V)?   C(1)

(b) What is the green colour due to in A?   C(1)

(c) (i) Why is a dark solution B obtained when A is acidified?   C(2)

    (ii) Write an ionic equation to show how A is converted into B.   C(2)

(d) What species of manganese is present in C?   C(1)

(e) Which solution, B or C, contains manganese in its highest oxidation state?   C(1)

(f) It was found that $10\,cm^3$ of a solution of C in water reacted with $20\,cm^3$ of acidified potassium iodide solution (concentration $0.05\,mol\,dm^{-3}$), but only $2\,cm^3$ when the potassium iodide was not acidified.

   (i) How many moles of potassium iodide were used when the solution was acidified and when the solution was not acidified?   C(2)

  (ii) What does this tell you about the oxidizing properties of solution C?   H(2)

 (iii) What colour would you expect the resulting solution to be after reaction between C and acidified potassium iodide solution?   K(1)

 (iv) The concentration of solution C was $0.02\,mol\,dm^{-3}$. Write an ionic equation showing the reaction between C and acidified potassium iodide solution.   H(2)

Total   15 marks

65 Reactions of iron

Study the reaction scheme below and then answer the questions.

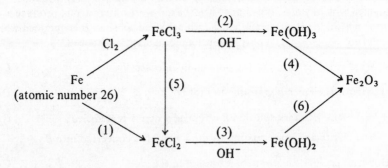

(a) What is the electronic configuration of

(i) iron?   C(1)

(ii) iron in $FeCl_3$?   C(1)

(b) (i) Explain briefly why iron can form more than one chloride.   C(2)

(ii) What are the two oxidation states shown by iron in these two compounds?   C(2)

(c) How can the following be achieved:

(i) conversion (1)?   K(2)

(ii) conversion (4)? What is the by-product?   C(2)

(d) What are the essential colour changes that you would observe in performing conversions

(i) (2) and (4)?   K(1)

(ii) (3) and (6)?   K(1)

(e) Look at the following redox potentials (expressed as half-cells).

$$Fe^{3+}(aq) + e^- \longrightarrow Fe^{2+}(aq) \qquad E^{\ominus} = +0.77 \text{ V}$$
$$V^{3+}(aq) + e^- \longrightarrow V^{2+}(aq) \qquad E^{\ominus} = +0.20 \text{ V}$$
$$Sn^{4+}(aq) + 2e^- \longrightarrow Sn^{2+}(aq) \qquad E^{\ominus} = +0.15 \text{ V}$$
$$H_2O_2(aq) + 2H^+(aq) + 2e^- \longrightarrow 2H_2O(l) \qquad E^{\ominus} = +2.77 \text{ V}$$

(i) Which species is the strongest reductant?   C(1)

(ii) Suggest two solutions which could be used in conversion (5).   H(2)

Total 15 marks

66 Complexes of iron*

Read the following carefully and then answer the questions.

When a few crystals of iron(III) chloride were dissolved in water, the solution obtained was pale yellow. On addition of concentrated hydrochloric acid the solution turned a deeper yellow. On addition to the latter solution of potassium thiocyanate solution a colour change to blood-red occurred.

Atomic number: Fe = 26

(a) What is the electronic configuration of iron in the iron(III) ion?　　C(1)

(b) (i) What are the ligands surrounding the central ion when iron(III) chloride is dissolved in water?　　K(1)

　　(ii) How many ligands surround the central ion?　　K(1)

(c) Explain why, when concentrated hydrochloric acid is added to the solution, there is a colour change.　　H(2)

(d) When monodentate ligands CNS^- are added, a further colour change occurs.

　　(i) What is a 'monodentate ligand'?　　K(2)

　　(ii) Draw the structure of the coordination complex so formed.　　H(2)

(e) The logarithm of the overall stability constant for the iron–thiocyanate complex is 7·1, while that for an iron–fluoride complex is 15·3.

　　(i) How is the stability constant defined in terms of a metal ion M^{n+} and a monodentate ligand L?　　K(2)

　　(ii) Which complex of iron is more stable, the thiocyanate or the fluoride? Give your reasons.　　C(2)

　　(iii) What would you expect to see if a solution of sodium fluoride were added to the iron–thiocyanate complex?　　H(1)

　　(iv) What is the stability constant of the iron–fluoride complex?　　C(1)

Total　15 marks

67 A complex of cobalt

The following passage is concerned with the preparation of a complex of cobalt.

Dissolve 12 g of potassium ethanedioate (oxalate) and 4 g of ethanedioic (oxalic) acid in 80 cm^3 of boiling water in a 250 cm^3 beaker. Then add slowly 4 g of cobalt(II) carbonate. A deep purple solution will be obtained containing the complex ion $[Co(C_2O_4)_2]^{2-}$. This solution should be cooled to 40 °C. Add slowly to this solution 10 g of lead(IV) oxide, stirring continuously and maintaining the temperature of the solution at 40–50 °C by standing the beaker in a water bath. Carefully add drop by drop 4 cm^3 of moderately concentrated ethanoic (acetic) acid. The solution should now turn dark green. Filter through a Hirsch suction funnel and slowly add 90 cm^3 of ethanol to the filtrate and allow it to crystallize. Filter again and allow the crystals to dry in the dark. Crystals of the complex $K_3[Co(C_2O_4)_3]$ are obtained.

(a) What is the oxidation state of cobalt in

    (i) the purple complex ion?   C(1)

    (ii) the final product?   C(1)

(b) What is the function of the lead(IV) oxide?   C(2)

(c) Explain briefly the advantage of using a Hirsch funnel compared with an ordinary funnel.   C(2)

(d) Why is ethanol added to the dark green solution after filtration?   C(2)

(e) Write an ionic equation to show the formation of the final complex ion $[Co(C_2O_4)_3]^{3-}$ from the complex ion $[Co(C_2O_4)_2]^{2-}$ using ethanedioate (oxalate) ions, lead(IV) oxide, and hydrogen ions.   C(2)

(f) Why are the crystals dried in the dark?   C(1)

(g) To what class of ligands do ethanedioate (oxalate) ions belong (e.g. monodentate, etc.)?   C(1)

(h) (i) Draw the structure of the final complex ion.   H(2)

    (ii) What is the coordination number of cobalt in this complex ion? C(1)

    (iii) The complex salt is optically active. How do you account for this?   H(2)

    (iv) State, giving your reasons, whether you would expect the sample of salt prepared by the above method to be optically active.   H(2)

    (v) What is a systematic name for the complex salt?   H(1)

Total   20 marks

68 Stability constants of a nickel complex*

The logarithms of the successive values of the stability constants for the Ni^{2+}-NH_3 system at 300 K are given below.

	K_1	K_2	K_3	K_4	K_5	K_6
Logarithm	2·67	2·12	1·61	1·07	0·63	−0·09

(a) What is meant by the term 'stability constant'?   K(2)

(b) Why are there six stability constants listed for the Ni^{2+}-NH_3 system?   C(1)

(c) What would be the ionic species involved in the equilibrium associated with K_2 if the measurements were carried out in aqueous solution?   H(2)

(d) What is the logarithm of the overall stability constant of the system?   H(2)

(e) What is the standard free energy change $\Delta G^\ominus$ for the following reaction at 300 K if $R = 8\cdot3\,J\,K^{-1}\,mol^{-1}$?

$$Ni^{2+} + 4NH_3 \rightleftharpoons [Ni(NH_3)_4]^{2+} \qquad\qquad H(3)$$

(f) The logarithm of first stability constant for the bidentate ligand 1,2-diaminoethane (en) and Ni^{2+} complex ion is 7·28.

  (i) What do you understand by the term 'bidentate'?   K(2)

  (ii) Compare the logarithm of the first stability constant of the Ni^{2+}-en ion with the stability constant obtained by adding the first two molecules of ammonia to the nickel solution.   H(2)

  (iii) Which of these systems is the more stable?   H(1)

Total   15 marks

69 A copper complex

Copper(II) ions form complex ions with molecules of 1,2-diaminoethane (en) as ligands of formula $[Cu(en)_x]^{2+}$. The complex ion so formed is highly coloured and provided that the maximum colour intensity coincides with the maximum number of complex ions formed it is possible to determine the number of ligands surrounding the central copper(II) ion. The following table gives some information of colorimeter readings obtained when various volumes of copper(II) sulphate(VI) were mixed with various volumes of 1,2-diaminoethane

Volume of $CuSO_4/cm^3$ (concentration of 0·1 mol dm^{-3})	6·0	5·0	4·5	4·0	3·5	3·0	2·0	1·0
Volume of 1,2-diamino-ethane/cm^3 (concentration 0·1 mol dm^{-3})	4·0	5·0	5·5	6·0	6·5	7·0	8·0	9·0
Colour intensity (colorimeter reading)	3·0	5·4	7·5	10·4	12·0	10·6	6·7	4·8

(a) (i) Plot a graph of the colorimeter reading against the volume of 1,2-diaminoethane solution, reading from right to left, and the volume of copper(II) sulphate(VI), reading from left to right. Carefully label the axes.   C(3)

   (ii) What volumes of the two solutions are needed to produce a maximum colour intensity?   C(2)

   (iii) What is the value of x in the formula of the complex ion? Give your reasons.   C(2)

   (iv) Write an equation to show how the complex ion is formed.   C(1)

(b) (i) Ligands are referred to as monodentate, bidentate, etc. What type of ligand is 1,2-diaminoethane?   K(1)

   (ii) Draw the structure of the complex produced in this case.   C(2)

   (iii) What is the coordination number of copper in this complex?   C(1)

   (iv) Write down an expression for the overall stability constant of the 1,2-diaminoethanecopper(II) complex.   H(2)

   (v) State, giving reasons, if you would expect the complex to be soluble in benzene.   H(1)

Total   15 marks

70 The determination of zinc

In an experiment to determine the concentration of zinc ions in an impure
sample of hydrated zinc sulphate(VI), 7 g of the zinc sulphate(VI) crystals were
dissolved in distilled water and then made up to $250 \, cm^3$. Then $25 \, cm^3$ of this
solution was pipetted into a conical flask and diluted with $100 \, cm^3$ of distilled
water. To this solution $2 \, cm^3$ of ammonium chloride–ammonia buffer solution
were added. Eriochrome Black T indicator was added to give the solution a
clear red colour. The resulting solution was then titrated with bis [di(carboxy-
methyl)amino] ethane (edta) (concentration $0 \cdot 1 \, mol \, dm^{-3}$) until the colour
changed to blue. It was found that $9 \, cm^3$ were required for the colour change.

Relative atomic masses: $0 = 16, S = 32, Zn = 65$

(a) What general name is given to the above type of titration? K (1)

(b) The following is the structure of edta.

Draw the structural formula of edta when it exists as its disodium
salt. C (2)

(c) Why was a buffer solution added? H (2)

(d) Why do you think that on adding the indicator to the solution the colour
of the indicator changed from black to red? H (2)

(e) Explain the reason for the colour change (red–blue) at the end point. H (2)

(f) (i) How many moles of edta were used in the titration? C (2)

(ii) If one mole of edta reacts with one mole of zinc ions, what is the
concentration (in $mol \, dm^{-3}$) of the zinc ions in the original $250 \, cm^3$
of solution? C (2)

(g) How can the presence of sulphate(VI) ions be detected in the original
solution? K (2)

Total   15 marks

71 Hydrocarbons I

The following is a list of hydrocarbons, all containing eight carbon atoms. The boiling points (K) of some of these hydrocarbons are also shown.

Hydrocarbon	Formula	Boiling point /K
Octane	C_8H_{18}	398
2,2,3,3-Tetramethylbutane	$CH_3-C(CH_3)_2-C(CH_3)_2-CH_3$	–
Ethylbenzene	$C_6H_5-CH_2-CH_3$	409
Phenylethene	$C_6H_5-CH=CH_2$	418
1,2-Dimethylbenzene	$C_6H_4(CH_3)_2$	417
1,2-Dimethylcyclohexane	$C_6H_{10}(CH_3)_2$	–
1,2-Dimethylcyclohex-1-ene	$C_6H_8(CH_3)_2$	–
Cyclooctatetraene	C_8H_8	413

(a) Octane and 2,2,3,3-tetramethylbutane are structural isomers, but many more exist.

    (i) What is a 'structural isomer'?   K(1)

    (ii) Draw the structural formula of another isomer of octane and name it.   H(2)

(b) Would you expect 2,2,3,3-tetramethylbutane to have a higher or lower boiling point than octane? Give your reasons.   H(2)

(c) Which hydrocarbon(s) require(s) the most hydrogen for complete hydrogenation?   H(2)

(d) When ethylbenzene is oxidized under suitable conditions a compound, A, of molecular formula $C_7H_6O_2$ is obtained, but when 1,2-dimethylbenzene is oxidized a compound, B, of molecular formula $C_8H_6O_4$ is obtained and when this is heated further a compound, C, of molecular formula $C_8H_4O_3$ is obtained.

    (i) What are the identities of $A, B,$ and C?   H(3)

    (ii) What are the 'suitable conditions'?   K(1)

(e) How would you distinguish chemically between a sample of 1,2-dimethyl-cyclohexane and a sample of 1,2-dimethylcyclohex-1-ene?   H(2)

(f) Cyclooctatetraene behaves chemically as a typical aliphatic alkene.

    (i) Give one reason why you think cyclooctatetraene behaves as an aliphatic alkene in view of the fact that it contains alternate single and double bonds.   H(1)

    (ii) Draw the structure of the molecule obtained when one mole of cyclo-octatetraene reacts with four moles of hydrogen bromide.   H(1)

         Total   15 marks

72 Hydrocarbons II

Look at the following list of hydrocarbons and then answer the questions. Use the letter code where applicable.

(A) $CH_2=C-CH=C\begin{smallmatrix} CH_3 \\ \\ H \end{smallmatrix}$
         $|$
       CH_3

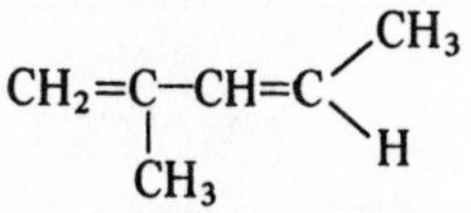

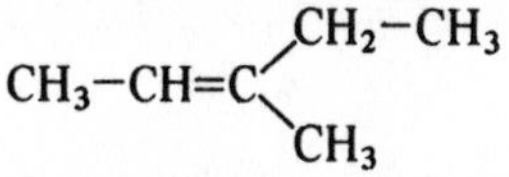

(B) $CH_3-CH-CH_2-CH-CH_3$
         $|$ $|$
       CH_3 CH_3

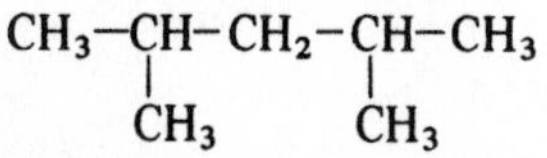

(C) $CH_3-CH_2-C\equiv C-H$

(D) $CH_3-CH=C\begin{smallmatrix} CH_2-CH_3 \\ \\ CH_3 \end{smallmatrix}$

(E) CH_2-CH_3
         $|$
   $H-C-CH_3$

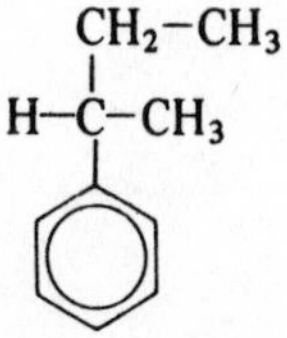

(a) Give the names of the hydrocarbons A and C.   C (2)

(b) Which of the compounds in the list will show

   (i) optical activity?   C (1)

   (ii) geometrical isomerism?   C (1)

(c) Draw another structural isomer of compound B.   H (1)

(d) Which of the above compounds will react with hydrogen in the mole ratio 1: 2?   C (2)

(e) Compound E can react with chlorine in two different ways: side-chain substitution and nuclear substitution.

   (i) What conditions are necessary for nuclear substitution?   K (2)

   (ii) What is the structural formula of the product obtained when compound E is reacted completely with chlorine for side-chain substitution?   C (1)

   (iii) What is the name of the product when E is oxidized by alkaline potassium manganate(VII) solution?   H (1)

(f) When compounds *A* and *D* undergo ozonolysis at the double bonds, followed by the addition of water and zinc dust, one of the organic products obtained is the same in each case.

   (i) Explain why this is so.   H(2)

   (ii) What are the names of the product when *D* undergoes these reactions?   H(2)

Total   15 marks

73 Phenylethene*

This question is concerned with phenylethene (styrene) and some of its properties. The structural formula of phenylethene is shown below.

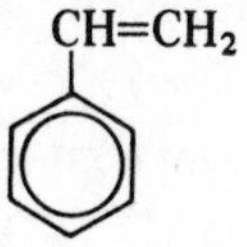

$CH=CH_2$

(a) A method of preparation of phenylethene is to heat a compound of molecular formula $C_8H_{10}O$ with concentrated sulphuric acid.

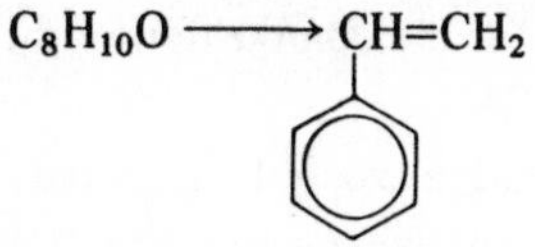

$$C_8H_{10}O \longrightarrow CH=CH_2$$

  (i) Draw two possible structures for the compound $C_8H_{10}O$.   H (2)

  (ii) Suggest a mechanism for the reaction.   H (2)

(b) One of the most convenient laboratory preparations of phenylethene is to heat 3-phenylpropenoic acid (cinnamic acid) with a small amount of benzene-1,4-diol (quinol) according to the following equation.

$$C_6H_5-CH=CH-COOH \longrightarrow C_6H_5-CH=CH_2 + CO_2$$

  (i) Draw the structural formula of benzene-1,4-diol.   C (1)

  (ii) Describe briefly how you would attempt to measure the rate of evolution of carbon dioxide at a temperature of, say, $100\,^{\circ}C$.   H (2)

(c) Phenylethene is manufactured industrially by the dehydrogenation of ethylbenzene at about 870 K using a catalyst such as zinc oxide.

  (i) Write an equation to show this process.   C (1)

  (ii) The starting material is not, however, ethylbenzene; it is benzene. How can ethylbenzene be obtained from benzene in the laboratory?   K (2)

(d) When phenylethene is boiled under air reflux in liquid paraffin as a solvent for about 30 minutes, a rubbery substance is obtained.

  (i) What is meant by the statement 'boiled under air reflux'?   K (1)

  (ii) What is the name given to the rubbery substance?   C (1)

  (iii) Draw a structure for this substance you have named.   C (1)

(e) How would you distinguish chemically between a sample of phenylethene and a sample of benzene?   C (2)

Total   15 marks

85

74 Determination of a hydrocarbon formula I

When 240 cm³ of a hydrocarbon were completely burnt in oxygen, it was found that 720 cm³ of carbon dioxide and 0·03 moles of water were produced. (All measurements were made at room temperature.)

Relative atomic masses: $H = 1$, $C = 12$, $O = 16$.

The molar volume of a gas at room temperature = 24 000 cm³

(a)   (i)   How many moles of hydrocarbon and how many moles of carbon dioxide were present?   C(2)

    (ii)   What is the molecular formula of the hydrocarbon?   H(1)

    (iii)   Write an equation for the combustion of the hydrocarbon in oxygen.   C(1)

    (iv)   What volume of oxygen would be required to burn the 240 cm³ of hydrocarbon?   C(1)

    (v)   What mass of water would be produced?   C(1)

    (vi)   Suggest two possible structural formulae for the hydrocarbon.   H(2)

(b) The hydrocarbon reacts with hydrogen bromide to give a compound of molecular formula C_3H_7Br.

    (i)   What is the structural formula of this compound?   H(1)

    (ii)   Suggest a mechanism for this reaction.   H(2)

(c) If the hydrocarbon underwent ozonolysis, which was followed by the addition of water and zinc dust, what would be the names of the organic compounds obtained?   H(2)

(d) What is meant by the term 'an isotactic polymer'? Illustrate your answer by considering the polymer obtained from the original hydrocarbon.   H(2)

Total   15 marks

75 Determination of a hydrocarbon formula II

When a hydrocarbon burns in oxygen, the combustion can be represented by a general equation in the following way.

$$C_xH_y(g) + (x + y/4)O_2(g) \longrightarrow xCO_2(g) + (y/2)H_2O(g)$$

When $20\,cm^3$ of a hydrocarbon C_xH_y were exploded with $200\,cm^3$ of oxygen in a suitable apparatus, it was found that on cooling back to room temperature the total volume of the gas remaining was $160\,cm^3$. When the remaining gas was shaken with aqueous sodium hydroxide, the resulting volume was $20\,cm^3$.

(a) (i)   What volume of carbon dioxide was produced by the explosion? C (1)

    (ii) What volume of oxygen was used in the explosion? C (1)

    (iii) What is the value of x? C (1)

    (iv) What is the value of y? C (1)

(b) It was found that when the hydrocarbon was burnt in air a large amount of smoke was produced. When the hydrocarbon was shaken with aqueous bromine no colour change was observed.

    (i)   Does this information indicate that the hydrocarbon is aromatic or aliphatic? Give your reasons. C (2)

    (ii) Suggest a structural formula for the hydrocarbon. C (1)

(c) A hydrocarbon with similar properties is ethylbenzene.

    (i)   Draw the structural formula of ethylbenzene. C (1)

    (ii) Write an equation for the complete combustion of ethylbenzene with oxygen. C (2)

(d) When ethylbenzene is heated with alkaline potassium manganate(VII) solution, the solution changed colour and, on cooling, a white crystalline solid was obtained.

    (i)   What colour changes would be observed? K (1)

    (ii) What is the identity of the white crystalline solid? C (1)

(e) Outline a possible reaction scheme to show how ethyl benzoate could be obtained from benzene. You may assume to have available only the following organic materials: iodoethane, ethanol, and benzene. Inorganic chemicals are freely available. H (3)

Total   15 marks

76 An unknown hydrocarbon*

A certain hydrocarbon was stated to contain 7·7 per cent hydrogen and 92·3 per cent carbon.

Relative atomic masses: $H = 1, C = 12, O = 16$.

(a) What is the empirical formula of the hydrocarbon?   C(2)

(b) An experiment was carried out to confirm the percentage of carbon; 0·078 g of the compound was burnt yielding 0·264 g of carbon dioxide.

   (i) Describe briefly how this information is obtained.   K(2)

   (ii) Do these data agree with those initially given?   H(2)

(c) The relative density of the hydrocarbon is 39.

   (i) What is the relative molecular mass of the hydrocarbon?   C(1)

   (ii) What is the molecular formula of the hydrocarbon?   H(1)

   (iii) Suggest two possible structures for the hydrocarbon.   H(2)

(d) When the hydrocarbon was nitrated by reacting it with a mixture of concentrated nitric(V) and sulphuric(VI) acids, a single product was identified.

   (i) Draw the structural formula of the product.   C(1)

   (ii) Why is a mixture of concentrated nitric(V) and sulphuric(VI) acids necessary to nitrate the hydrocarbon?   K(2)

   (iii) Suggest a mechanism for the reaction.   H(2)

Total   15 marks

77 2-Bromo-2-methylpropane*

When 0.6 cm^3 of 2-bromo-2-methylpropane reacted with a mixture of water and methanol containing potassium hydroxide, a fast reaction took place with the evolution of a gas. The gas was found to decolorize an aqueous solution of bromine.

Relative atomic masses: H = 1, C = 12, Br = 80
The molar volume of gas at room temperature = 24 000 cm³

(a) What is the structural formula of 2-bromo-2-methylpropane?   C (1)

(b) Why do you think methanol was used in the reaction?   C (1)

(c) Which organic grouping(s) decolorize(s) an aqueous solution of bromine?   K (1)

(d) (i) What is the name and structural formula of the gaseous product in the reaction?   H (2)

    (ii) Suggest another organic compound derived from 2-bromo-2-methyl-propane which may be found in the reaction vessel.   H (1)

(e) The density of 2-bromo-2-methylpropane is 1.2 g cm^{-3}.

    (i) What mass of 2-bromo-2-methylpropane was reacted?   C (1)

    (ii) How many moles does this represent?   C (2)

    (iii) How many moles of gas would be obtained?   C (1)

    (iv) What volume of gas would be obtained?   C (1)

    (v) If the volume of gas collected was 25 cm^3, what is the percentage yield of the gas?   C (2)

(f) Sketch a suitable piece of apparatus for performing the experiment.   H (2)

Total   15 marks

78 Synthetic uses of haloalkanes*

The following reaction scheme represents the possible use of a haloalkane of *molecular* formula C_3H_7Br in organic syntheses.

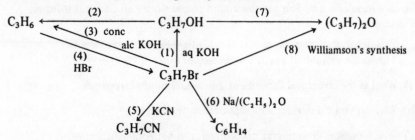

(a) Draw two possible structural formulae for C_3H_7Br.   C (2)

(b) Write an equation using structural formulae to show how hydrogen bromide reacts with the alkene C_3H_6.   C (2)

(c) What is the actual structure of the bromoalkane?   C (1)

(d) What is the name of the hydrocarbon formed in reaction (6)?   C (1)

(e) To what class of organic reactions does reaction (3) belong?   K (1)

(f) Reaction (1) can take place by two different mechanisms known as S_N1 and S_N2. Explain the difference between these two mechanisms.   H (4)

(g) (i) Suggest a suitable solvent for reaction (5). Give your reasons.   C (2)

  (ii) What organic product is formed when the product of reaction (5) is hydrolyzed with dilute hydrochloric acid?   C (1)

(h) A further use of haloalkanes is in the preparation of ethers (e.g. reaction 8); this is known as the Williamson's synthesis. It involves reacting an alkoxide with a haloalkane.

  (i) What is an alkoxide?   K (1)

  (ii) Which alkoxide must be reacted with the bromoalkane C_3H_7Br in order that an ether of molecular formula $(C_3H_7)_2O$ is obtained? H (1)

  (iii) Using structural formulae write an equation for the preparation of the ether in reaction (8).   C (2)

(i) How and under what conditions is reaction (7) achieved?   K (2)

Total   20 marks

79 Aromatic hydrocarbons and their chloro derivatives

The relationship between benzene, methylbenzene (toluene), and their chloro derivatives is given in the diagram below.

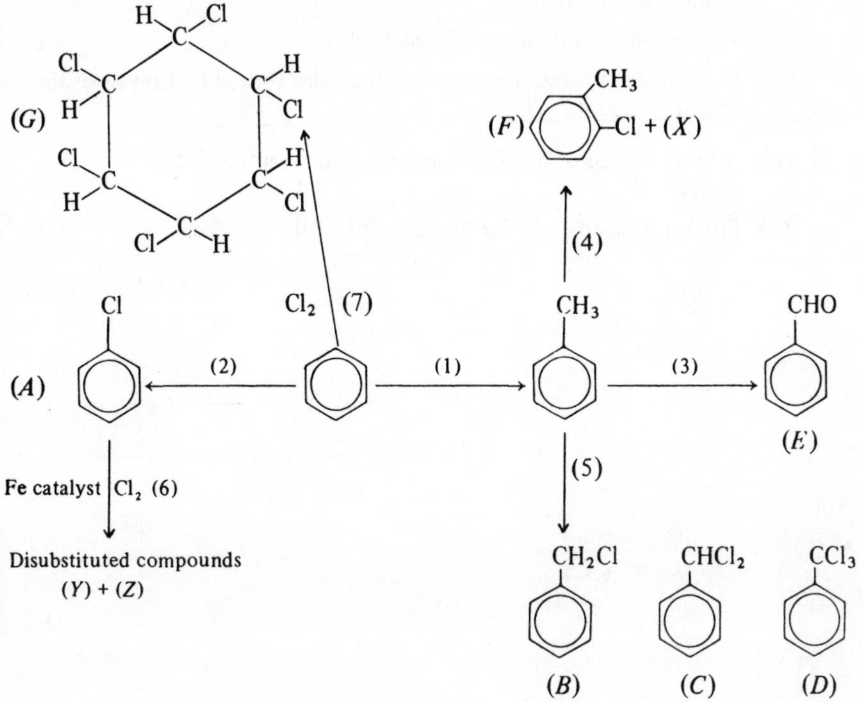

(a) What is the name of substance X?   C(1)

(b) Draw the structural formulae of substances Y and Z.   C(2)

(c) How and under what conditions are reactions (2) and (4) achieved?   K(4)

(d) If methylbenzene were chlorinated in the presence of ultraviolet light, an iron catalyst, and at a temperature of 40 °C, what do you think the products of the reaction would be? Give reasons for your answer.   H(2)

(e) When chlorobenzene (A) and (chloromethyl) benzene (B) were added separately to portions of aqueous silver nitrate containing dilute nitric acid only one of these substances produced a white precipitate on shaking for 15 minutes.

   (i) Explain why the white precipitate was produced.   C(2)

   (ii) Which substance produced the white precipitate?   C(1)

91

(f) When one mole of methylbenzene was chlorinated under suitable conditions, an organic product was obtained together with two moles of hydrogen chloride. The organic product underwent rapid hydrolysis to benzaldehyde (*E*).

    (i) Write down the letter which corresponds to the formula of the organic product on chlorination.   C(1)

    (ii) What are the 'suitable conditions'?   K(2)

    (iii) Write an equation using structural formulae for the hydrolysis of the organic product.   C(1)

(g)   (i) Into what class of organic reactions would reaction (7) be placed?   K(1)

    (ii) Propose a mechanism for the first part of the reaction.   H(3)

Total   20 marks

80 Alcohols

The following table gives the enthalpies of combustion of some aliphatic alcohols.

Alcohol		Enthalpy of combustion /kJ mol^{-1}
Methanol	CH_3OH	-726
Ethanol	C_2H_5OH	-1366
Propan-1-ol	C_3H_7OH	-2026
Butan-1-ol	C_4H_9OH	-2676

(a) (i) Plot a graph of the enthalpy of combustion (vertical axis) against the number of carbon atoms in each alcohol (horizontal axis).   C (2)

  (ii) Use your graph to obtain an estimate of the enthalpy of combustion of pentan-1-ol.   C (1)

 (iii) What is the average enthalpy of combustion of a $-CH_2$ group using the alcohols listed?   C (2)

 (iv) What is an approximate value for the enthalpy of combustion of the (C$-$H) bond?   C (1)

(b) The alcohols listed are said to constitute part of an homologous series. This means, for example, that all members can be represented by a general formula.

  (i) What is the general formula of the alcohols?   K (1)

  (ii) Suggest two other general properties of homologous series.   K (2)

(c) Propanol can exist as two structural isomers.

  (i) What is meant by a 'structural isomer'?   K (1)

  (ii) Draw the structural formulae of the two isomers of propanol.   C (2)

 (iii) What chemical test would you perform in order to distinguish between these two isomers?   H (2)

(d) One of the structural isomers of butanol is optically active. Draw a structural formula to show this isomer.   H (1)

Total   15 marks

81 Hydroxy compounds and ethers*

The following question is concerned with three structural isomers of molecular formula C_7H_8O.

CH_2-OH

CH_3 OH

$O-CH_3$

(A)   (B)   (C)

(a) Name compounds A, B, and C.   C (3)

(b) Two further structural isomers of molecular formula C_7H_8O exist.
    Write down their structural formulae.   C (2)

(c) (i) Both A and B react with metallic sodium to produce ionic compounds.
        Does this information indicate whether A and B are acidic or alkaline
        in character? State which and give your reasons.   C (2)

    (ii) Compound B reacts with aqueous sodium hydrogencarbonate to form
         carbon dioxide, whereas A does not. What can you now deduce about
         the relative acidity or alkalinity of A and B.   H (2)

(d) When compound A is oxidized a compound of molecular formula $C_7H_6O_2$
    is obtained, whereas when B is oxidized a compound of molecular formula
    $C_7H_6O_3$ is obtained. What are the identities of the oxidation products
    of A and B?   H (2)

(e) When compound A, benzoic acid, and a few drops of concentrated
    sulphuric(VI) acid are reacted together an ester is formed.

    (i) Write an equation using structural formulae to show this
        reaction.   C (1)

    (ii) Propose a mechanism for this reaction.   H (2)

    (iii) In order to esterify compound B a different technique is used.
          Describe how this is achieved.   K (2)

(f) Given separate unlabelled samples of A and C, describe a chemical test
    that you would perform in order to distinguish between the two
    samples.   H (2)

(g) Which of the three isomers, A, B, or C, would you expect to have the lowest
    boiling point? Give your reasons.   H (2)

                                                            Total   20 marks

82 Analysis of a given compound*

A chemist claims to have made a compound with the following structure.

$$HO-\langle\bigcirc\rangle-CH=C(CH_3)-CH_2-O-CH_3$$
$$\hspace{3.5cm}CH_2-OH$$

He found that his compound had a low boiling point and reacted with sodium with evolution of hydrogen, but did not colour iron(III) chloride solution.
It dissolved in concentrated hydrochloric acid.

(a) If one mole of the compound was reacted with sodium, how many moles of hydrogen would be produced?   H(1)

(b) How would you expect the compound to react with

   (i) aqueous bromine?   H(2)

   (ii) hydrogen bromide?   H(2)

(c) Suggest reasons why the compound dissolved in concentrated hydrochloric acid.   H(2)

(d) (i) Which piece of evidence suggests that the structure drawn may be incorrect?   H(1)

   (ii) Draw another structure for the compound that would eliminate the error.   H(1)

(e) It was found by the chemist that the molecule could be esterified with ethanoic (acetic) acid and concentrated sulphuric(VI) acid.

   (i) Which functional group would be esterified?   K(1)

   (ii) How many moles of ethanoic acid would be required to esterify the molecule originally drawn? Give your reasons.   H(2)

   (iii) How many moles of ethanoic acid would be required to esterify the molecule in (d)(ii)?   H(1)

(f) Suggest, giving your reasons, a physical technique which might be used to assist in the assignment of the correct structure.   H(2)

Total   15 marks

83 Preparation of a phenylhydrazone

The following instructions were given in a typical chemistry practical book for the preparation of the phenylhydrazone of an aldehyde.

Prepare a water bath using a 500 cm³ beaker containing water heated almost to boiling. Dissolve 0·53 g of the aldehyde in the *minimum* amount of *hot* ethanol in a test tube. Add this solution to 5 cm³ of phenylhydrazine in a test tube, with shaking. Heat the tube in the water bath for five minutes, shaking occasionally. Cool the tube under the tap and filter the crude material under reduced pressure, washing it with a little cold water. Recrystallize the crude material from the minimum amount of hot aqueous ethanol (1:2 by volume). Allow to cool to room temperature and again filter the pure crystals under reduced pressure. Finally allow the crystals to dry in the air and then determine the melting point.

Relative atomic masses: H = 1, C = 12, N = 14, O = 16.

(a) What is the function of the water bath? K(1)

(b) Why is the aldehyde dissolved in the minimum amount of alcohol? C(2)

(c) Why is the tube containing the aldehyde, alcohol, and phenylhadrazine heated? C(1)

(d) Why is this tube and contents allowed to cool before filtration? C(1)

(e) Suggest why 'normal pressure' is not used in the filtration process. C(1)

(f) Suggest a reason for using aqueous ethanol, rather than pure ethanol in the recrystallization. H(2)

(g) Describe briefly how you would determine the melting point of the product. K(3)

(h) Into what class of organic reactions would the preparation of the aldehyde-phenylhydrazone be placed? K(1)

(I) (i) Draw the structural formula of phenylhydrazine. K(1)

(ii) If the aldehyde taken was benzaldehyde, write an equation using structural formulae for the preparation of the phenylhydrazone of benzaldehyde. C(2)

(iii) What fraction of a mole does 0.53 g of benzaldehyde represent? H(2)

(iv) How many moles of the phenylhydrazone of benzaldehyde would be produced? H(1)

(v) What would be the theoretical mass of the phenylhydrazone obtained? H(2)

Total   20 marks

84 Carbonyl compounds

The following is a list of compounds all containing the carbonyl group.

(A) $\begin{array}{c} H \\ \diagdown \\ H \diagup \end{array} C=O$ (B) $\begin{array}{c} CH_3 \\ \diagdown \\ H \diagup \end{array} C=O$ (C) $\begin{array}{c} CH_3 \\ \diagdown \\ CH_3 \diagup \end{array} C=O$

(D) $\begin{array}{c} C_2H_5 \\ \diagdown \\ H \diagup \end{array} C=O$ (E) $\begin{array}{c} C_2H_5 \\ \diagdown \\ CH_3 \diagup \end{array} C=O$

In the questions below, use the assigned letters, if applicable.

(a) Which in the above list are ketones?   K (2)

(b) What is the name of substance E?   C (1)

(c) Which two compounds are structural isomers?   H (2)

(d) A positive triiodomethane (iodoform) test is given by compounds which contain the CH_3CO-group attached to either a hydrogen, alkyl, or aryl group, or are oxidized to this structure by the reagents.

   (i) What are the reagents in the triiodomethane test?   K (1)

   (ii) Which of the compounds in the list would give a positive triiodomethane test?   H (3)

(e) Describe a suitable test that you would perform in order to distinguish between B and C.   C (2)

(f) An acidified potassium dichromate(VI) solution was added to D and then the mixture was warmed.

   (i) What would you see happening?   K (1)

   (ii) What would be the name of the organic product obtained?   C (1)

(g) Some carbonyl compounds with hydrogen cyanide form addition compounds called cyanohydrins.

   (i) Select one of the carbonyl compounds listed and using structural formulae show how an addition compound can be formed.   C (1)

   (ii) How can 2-hydroxypropanoic (lactic) acid be obtained from B? H (1)

Total   15 marks

85 The manufacture of ethanal

Read the following extract† and then answer the questions.

Ethanal (acetaldehyde) is manufactured in the UK by the processes summarized in the following equations:

(1) $CH_3-CH_2OH + \frac{1}{2}OH + \frac{1}{2}O_2 \xrightarrow[550°C]{Ag} CH_3-CHO + H_2O$ (exothermic)

$CH_3-CH_2OH \xrightarrow[550°C]{Ag} CH_3-CHO + H_2$ (endothermic)

(2) $CH_3-CH_2OH \xrightarrow[275-300°C]{Cu} CH_3-CHO + H_2$

These processes are now diminishing and a new process (devised by Wacker) has been developed in Germany for the manufacture of carbonyl compounds from alkenes, in particular ethanal from ethene, propanone (acetone) from propene and butanone (ethyl methyl ketone) from but-1-ene. In the ethanal process, ethene and oxygen at moderate pressure are passed into a solution containing palladium(II) chloride and copper(II) chloride at pH 1-2 and 20-60°C.

(3) $CH_2=CH_2 + PdCl_2 + H_2O \longrightarrow CH_3-CHO + Pd + 2HCl$

(4) $Pd + 2HCl + \frac{1}{2}O_2 \longrightarrow PdCl_2 + H_2O$

The palladium(II) chloride solution thus acts as an oxygen carrier. The purpose of the copper(II) chloride is to promote the much slower second reaction, (4).

(5) $2CuCl_2 + Pd \longrightarrow 2CuCl + PdCl_2$

(6) $2CuCl + 2HCl + \frac{1}{2}O_2 \longrightarrow 2CuCl_2 + H_2O$

(7) $CH_2 = CH_2 + 2CuCl_2 + H_2O \xrightarrow{PdCl_2} CH_3 -CHO + 2HCl + 2CuCl$

(8) $2CuCl + 2HCl + \frac{1}{2}O_2 \longrightarrow 2CuCl_2 + H_2O$

(a) Why do you think the reaction is performed at 550°C in the UK process? H(1)

(b) Suggest a possible reason why the German process may eventually replace the one in the UK. H(2)

(c) The enthalpies of formation of ethanol and ethanal are −280 and −190 kJ mol^{-1} respectively. What is the enthalpy change for reaction (2)? State clearly whether the reaction is endothermic or exothermic. H(3)

---

†Adapted from D. M. Samuel, *Industrial Chemistry – Organic* 2nd edn, R.I.C., 1972.

(d) Equation (5) can be regarded as a redox equation.

    (i) Which of the species is reduced?   C (1)

    (ii) Write an ionic equation for the conversion of palladium into palladium(II) chloride.   C (1)

(e)   (i) Write down the structural formulae of propanone and propene.   C (2)

    (ii) Write an equation (similar to equation 7) to show how butanone is obtained from but-1-ene.   C (1)

(f)   (i) Give the essential experimental details of how ethanal is prepared in the laboratory from ethanol.   K (2)

    (ii) Given separate samples of ethanal and ethanol, describe a chemical test that you could perform in order to distinguish between them.   H (2)

Total   15 marks

86 Preparation of ethanoic acid

The following practical instructions for the preparation of ethanoic (acetic) acid were found in a typical chemistry practical textbook.

> To 10 cm³ of water in a boiling flask, add slowly, with shaking and cooling, 6 cm³ of concentrated sulphuric(VI) acid. Dissolve completely 10 g of sodium dichromate(VI) in the solution and add a few granules of pumice, and then fit a reflux condenser to the flask. In a separate container make a mixture of 4 cm³ of ethanol and 10 cm³ of water and add this a little at a time (using a teat pipette) to the reaction mixture through the condenser. The reaction may become violent; in this case cool the flask in a water bath. When all the aqueous alcohol has been added heat the flask in a water bath and reflux for about 30 minutes. Allow the flask to cool and then distil the fraction boiling between 115 and 120 °C.
>
> Relative atomic masses: H = 1, C = 12, O = 16.

(a) Why is the concentrated sulphuric(VI) acid added to water before the addition of the alcohol? $\qquad$ C(1)

(b) What is the function of the pumice? $\qquad$ C(1)

(c) (i) If the density of ethanol is 0·80 g cm⁻³, what fraction of a mole does 4 cm³ of ethanol represent? $\qquad$ C(2)

(ii) How many moles of ethanoic acid would be formed in the reaction? Give your reasons. $\qquad$ C(2)

(iii) If the density of ethanoic acid is 1·1 g cm⁻³, what volume of ethanoic acid would you expect to be collected? $\qquad$ C(2)

(iv) The actual volume collected was 15 cm³. Explain the difference between this and your last answer. $\qquad$ H(1)

(d) (i) What organic impurities are likely to be found in the distillate? H(2)

(ii) Describe briefly how you would show the presence of one of these impurities in the distillate. $\qquad$ H(2)

(e) Assuming that the ethanoic acid could be further purified, describe how you would show that the product was ethanoic acid. $\qquad$ H(2)

Total   15 marks

87 Acid derivatives*

The following list of compounds are all derivatives of organic acids.

(A)   COCl
           ⬡ (benzene ring)

(B) $COOCH_3$
           OH
           ⬡ (benzene ring)

(C) $CH_3-CO-NH_2$

(D) $CH_3-CO-OOC-CH_2-CH_3$

(E) $COOC_2H_5$
           ⬡ (benzene ring)

(F) $CH_3-CH_2-CH_2-COCl$

(a) Which compounds in the above list are esters?   C (2)

(b) What is the name of compound E?   C (1)

(c) Which compounds in the above list would produce benzoic acid on acid hydrolysis?   H (2)

(d) If compounds A, D, and F are reacted with ethanol in a suitable way, esters are produced.

  (i) Choose any *one* of these and write an equation to show how an ester is produced.   C (1)

  (ii) Select *another* compound from A, D, or F and draw the structural formula of the ester formed with methanol.   C (1)

(e) (i) What is formed when compound F reacts with ammonia?   C (1)

  (ii) How can this product be converted into $CH_3-CH_2-CH_2-NH_2$?   H (2)

(f) How could you distinguish between B and E?   H (1)

(g) When compound C was reacted with sodium and ethanol a compound X was produced. When X was reacted with nitric(III) (nitrous) acid, nitrogen was evolved and a compound Y was produced. When Y was reacted with A, compound E was produced. By means of three equations, using structural formulae, show how these compounds are interrelated, carefully labelling each compound in each reaction.   H (4)

Total   15 marks

88 An organic reaction scheme

Study the following reaction scheme and then answer the questions.

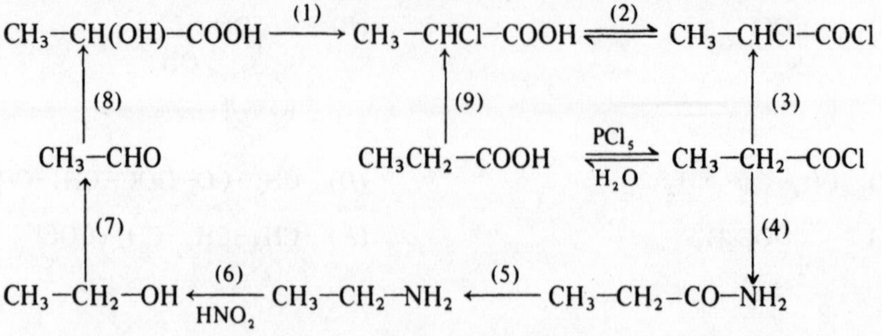

$CH_3-CH(OH)-COOH \xrightarrow{(1)} CH_3-CHCl-COOH \underset{(2)}{\rightleftharpoons} CH_3-CHCl-COCl$

$\Big\uparrow (8) \qquad \qquad \Big\uparrow (9) \qquad \qquad \Big\uparrow (3)$

$CH_3-CHO \qquad CH_3CH_2-COOH \underset{H_2O}{\overset{PCl_5}{\rightleftharpoons}} CH_3-CH_2-COCl$

$\Big\uparrow (7) \qquad \qquad \qquad \qquad \qquad \Big\downarrow (4)$

$CH_3-CH_2-OH \underset{HNO_2}{\overset{(6)}{\longleftarrow}} CH_3-CH_2-NH_2 \overset{(5)}{\longleftarrow} CH_3-CH_2-CO-NH_2$

(a) Which compounds in the reaction scheme would show optical activity? C(3)

(b) Which conversion represents a Hofmann degradation? C(1)

(c) Which conversion represents an oxidation? C(1)

(d) What do you think would happen when the compound $CH_3-CHCl-COCl$ was

   (i) added to water? H(1)

   (ii) boiled with dilute sodium hydroxide solution? H(2)

(e) (i) Name the compound $CH_3-CH(OH)-COOH$. C(1)

   (ii) Would you classify the $-OH$ group in $CH_3-CH(OH)-COOH$ as primary, secondary, or tertiary? C(1)

   (iii) On the basis of this answer write down the structural formula of the compound obtained when $CH_3-CH(OH)-COOH$ is oxidized using potassium dichromate(VI) and sulphuric(VI) acid. H(1)

(f) (i) How are conversions (3) and (9) achieved? H(1)

   (ii) How is conversion (4) achieved? H(1)

(g) Three acids are given in the reaction scheme. Which one do you think is the strongest acid? Give your reasons. H(2)

Total   15 marks

89 Organic bases*

The following table gives values for the ionization constants K_b for some organic bases and ammonia in aqueous solution.

Name	Formula	K_b /mol dm^{-3}	pK_b
Ammonia	NH_3	1.6×10^{-5}	4·8
Methylamine	CH_3NH_2	4.0×10^{-4}	3·4
Ethylamine	$C_2H_5NH_2$	5.0×10^{-4}	3·3
Dimethylamine	$(CH_3)_2NH$	6.3×10^{-4}	3·2
Diethylamine	$(C_2H_5)_2NH$	7.9×10^{-4}	3·1
Phenylamine	$C_6H_5NH_2$	4.0×10^{-10}	–
–	$C_6H_5NHCH_3$	2.5×10^{-10}	9·6

(a) (i) How are K_b and pK_b related? K (1)

   (ii) What is the pK_b value for phenylamine? C (2)

   (iii) Which of the compounds in the table in the strongest base? C (1)

(b) The strength of an organic base R_2NH in water may be estimated by considering the following equilibrium.

$$R_2NH + H_2O \rightleftharpoons R_2\overset{+}{N}H_2 + OH^-$$

   (i) Write down the expression for the equilibrium constant K_b for the base dimethylamine. H (1)

   (ii) The concentration of water is usually omitted from this expression. Can you suggest a reason for this? C (1)

(c) Explain the following statements.

   (i) The pK_b of ammonia is 4·8 whereas the pK_b of methylamine is 3·4. H (2)

   (ii) The pK_b of dimethylamine is 3·2 whereas the pK_b of methylamine is 3·4. H (2)

(d) (i) Why does phenylamine dissolve in hydrochloric acid, but not in water? H (2)

   (ii) Suggest why ethylamine does not react with bromine water, but phenylamine reacts to produce a white precipitate. C (2)

   (iii) What is the name of the compound having the formula $C_6H_5NHCH_3$? C (1)

Total   15 marks

90 Benzamide

Benzamide is a white solid having the formula

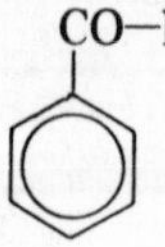

$$CO-NH_2$$

Relative atomic masses: H = 1, C = 12, N = 14, O = 16.

(a) If benzamide is heated with aqueous sodium hydroxide, after a short time ammonia can be detected. Explain the two-stage process involved in the formation of ammonia.   C (2)

(b) (i) Explain how the percentage of nitrogen in benzamide could be determined experimentally.   K (3)

     (ii) Calculate the percentage of nitrogen in benzamide.   C (2)

(c) When benzamide is treated with bromine and aqueous sodium hydroxide solution, after purification a liquid can be obtained of molecular formula C_6H_7N.

     (i) What name is given to this reaction?   K (1)

     (ii) What is the structural formula of the liquid?   H (1)

     (iii) Write an equation to show what happens when the liquid is reacted with ethanoyl (acetyl) chloride.   H (1)

(d) Sulphanilamide (4-aminobenzenesulphonamide) and its derivatives have great antibacterial powers. Sulphanilamide can be prepared by means of the following reaction scheme.

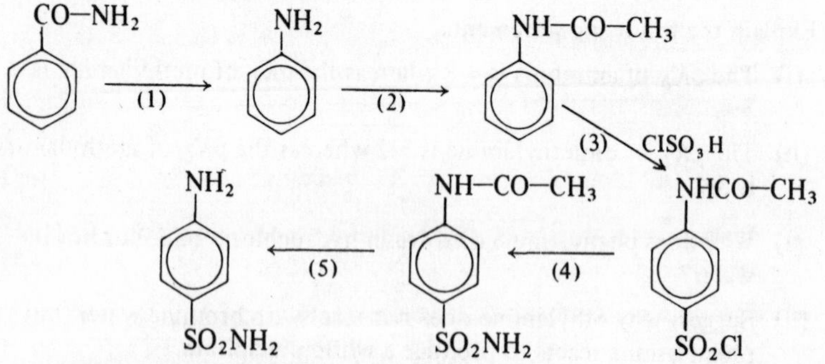

     (i) Explain briefly why the $-SO_2Cl$ group enters at position 4 in the benzene ring.   K (2)

     (ii) Explain briefly how reaction (4) could be achieved.   H (1)

     (iii) Explain how reaction (5) could be achieved. Include an equation in your answer.   H (2)

     Total   15 marks

91 An organic dye*

A large number of dyestuffs are characterized by the presence of an azo
(−N=N−) group in the molecule and are usually prepared by diazotizing a primary
aromatic amine with nitric(III) (nitrous) acid and then coupling the resulting
diazonium salt with a phenol or aromatic amine. During the coupling process
the pH of the solution is maintained at a particular value, depending on the
nature of the coupling component; for example, a pH of 4–5 is used for
aromatic amines and about 9 for phenols and naphthols. The following molecule
(1-amino-8-naphthol-3,6-disulphonic acid) is often a starting point for many
azo dyes.

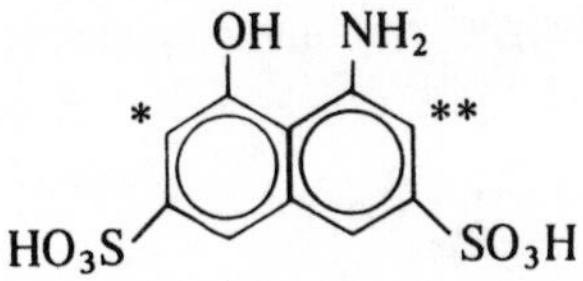

*indicates the position of coupling under alkaline conditions.
**indicates the position of coupling under acid conditions.

(a) (i) Describe briefly how you would prepare the diazonium salt of
phenylamine (aniline) using sodium nitrate(III) (nitrite) and
hydrochloric acid. Include an equation in your answer.　　　C (3)

   (ii) This diazonium salt was then coupled in alkaline conditions to the
molecule shown above. Draw the resulting structure.　　　H (1)

(b) (i) Draw the structural formula of 4-nitrophenylamine.　　　C (1)

   (ii) What is the structural formula of the diazonium salt obtained when
4-nitrophenylamine is diazotized with sodium nitrate(III)
and hydrochloric acid?　　　H (1)

   (iii) What is the structure of the dye obtained when 1-amino-8-naphthol-
3,6-disulphonic acid is first coupled with diazotized 4-nitrophenylamine
under acid conditions and then with diazotized phenylamine in
sodium carbonate solution?　　　H (2)

   (iv) How many azo groups are there in this structure?　　　C (1)

(c) (i) Depending on the structure, the dye has a particular colour.
Why should the dye appear coloured at all?　　　K (2)

   (ii) Why do some dyes appear black?　　　C (1)

(d) (i) Describe what would be seen if the solution prepared in (a) (i) was ·
warmed gently?　　　K (1)

   (ii) Write an equation for this reaction.　　　C (1)

(e)　How could the compound obtained in (b) (ii) be converted into
4-nitrochlorobenzene?　　　H (1)

Total　15 marks

92 Glycine*

Glycine (aminoethanoic acid) is the simplest amino acid, having the formula

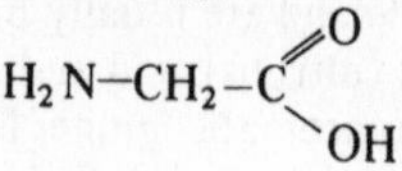

$$H_2N-CH_2-C\begin{smallmatrix} O \\ OH \end{smallmatrix}$$

(a) Why is glycine termed an amino acid?   K(1)

(b) Glycine itself is not optically active. Draw another amino acid which would be optically active and name it.   H(2)

(c) In solution glycine undergoes the following reactions, depending on the pH of the solution.

$$H_3\overset{+}{N}CH_2COOH \xleftarrow[+H^+]{acid} H_3\overset{+}{N}CH_2COO^- \xrightarrow[+OH^-]{alkali} H_2NCH_2COO^- + H_2O$$

(i) What is the general name of ions similar to $H_3\overset{+}{N}CH_2COO^-$?   K(1)

(ii) When $H_3\overset{+}{N}CH_2COO^-$ is the predominant species in solution, migration to either a cathode or anode under an applied field is not possible, and the pH at this electrical neutrality is known as the 'isoelectric point'. What technique is used to study isoelectric points?   K(1)

(iii) When alkali is added to $H_3\overset{+}{N}CH_2COO^-$, the ion is acting as an acid. Write down an expression for the equilibrium constant for the acid K_1 in terms of $H_3\overset{+}{N}CH_2COO^-$, H^+, and $H_2NCH_2COO^-$.   H(2)

(iv) Write down a similar expression for the base K_2 in terms of $H_3\overset{+}{N}CH_2COO^-$, H^+, and $H_3\overset{+}{N}CH_2COOH$.   H(2)

(v) At the isoelectric point the concentrations of the ions are equal, i.e. $[H_3\overset{+}{N}CH_2COOH] = [H_2NCH_2COO^-]$. By substituting for $H_3\overset{+}{N}CH_2COOH$ and $H_2NCH_2COO^-$, obtain an expression for pH (*isoelectric*) in terms of pK_1 and pK_2.   H(3)

(vi) If the pK_1 and pK_2 values of glycine are 2·4 and 9·6 respectively, what is the pH (*isoelectric*) of glycine?   H(1)

(d) Explain why glycine has a boiling point of 559 K, which is high compared with other compounds of similar relative molecular mass, e.g. chloroethanoic acid 462 K, and phenylamine, 457 K.   H(2)

Total   15 marks

93 Amino acids and peptides*

The following is a list of amino acids together with their formulae and codes.

Amino acid	Code	Formula
Glycine	gly	H_2N-CH_2-COOH
Alanine	ala	$H_2N-\overset{\displaystyle H}{\underset{\displaystyle CH_3}{C}}-COOH$
Serine	ser	$H_2N-\overset{\displaystyle H}{\underset{\displaystyle \underset{\displaystyle OH}{CH_2}}{C}}-COOH$

(a) Give a systematic name for

   (i) alanine.   H(1)

   (ii) serine.   H(1)

(b) When two different amino acids are joined via a peptide link to form a dipeptide, two possible structures can occur.

   (i) What is a 'peptide link'?   K(1)

   (ii) What are the two possible structures produced when glycine and alanine are joined together?   H(2)

   (iii) How many possible arrangements exist when three amino acids are joined together to form a tripeptide?   C(1)

(c) A tripeptide formed from glycine, alanine, and serine was subjected to acid hydrolysis.

   (i) How could the three amino acids be identified in the hydrolyzed sample?   K(2)

   (ii) Two dipeptides were also found in the hydrolyzed sample; these are given below.

$$H_2NCH_2-CO-NH-CH(CH_2OH)-COOH$$
$$H_2NCH(CH_2OH)-CO-NH-CH(CH_3)-COOH$$

Using the codes provided, what is the sequence of the amino acids in the tripeptide?   H(2)

(d) It is possible to distinguish between two dipeptides using 1-fluoro-2,4-dinitrobenzene. This technique is known as the N-terminal analysis of a dipeptide. Describe the technique as applied to the dipeptides in (c)(ii).   H(3)

(e) How are the structures of amino acids, peptides, and proteins related?   C(2)

Total   15 marks

94 Sucrose

Sucrose is a disaccharide. On dilute acid hydrolysis it produces an equimolar mixture of D(+)-glucose (a six-membered ring) and D(−)-fructose (a five-membered ring). The structural formula of sucrose is given below.

Relative atomic masses: H = 1, C = 12, O = 16

(a) Why is sucrose classified as a disaccharide?   K (1)

(b) What is the molecular formula of sucrose?   C (1)

(c) Draw the structural formulae of D(+)-glucose and D(−)-fructose.   C (2)

(d) What do the symbols (+) and (−) refer to in the naming of the compounds?   K (2)

(e)   (i) Write an equation to show how ethanoic (acetic) anhydride reacts with ethanol.   C (1)

   (ii) How many moles of ethanoic anhydride would be required to react with one mole of sucrose?   H (1)

  (iii) How many moles of ethanoic anhydride would be required to react with one mole each of D(+)-glucose and D(−)-fructose?   H (2)

(f) How much glucose would be obtained by hydrolyzing 17·1 g of sucrose?   H (3)

(g) In some of its reactions glucose behaves as an aldehyde and fructose as a ketone. Describe how you would distinguish chemically between a sample of glucose and fructose.   H (2)

Total   15 marks

95 Polymers I

The following table gives some monomer units and the polymer units that result from their polymerization.

Monomer	Polymer	Name of polymer
$H_2C=CH_2$	$-\overset{\displaystyle H}{\underset{\displaystyle H}{C}}-\overset{\displaystyle H}{\underset{\displaystyle H}{C}}-$	poly(ethene)
$CH=CH_2$ ⬡	$-\overset{\displaystyle H}{\underset{\displaystyle }{C}}-\overset{\displaystyle H}{\underset{\displaystyle H}{C}}-$ ⬡	
$H_2C=C(CH_3)COOCH_3$	–	poly(methyl 2-methyl-propenoate)
$F_2C=CF_2$	$\overset{\displaystyle F}{\underset{\displaystyle F}{C}}-\overset{\displaystyle F}{\underset{\displaystyle F}{C}}-$	–
–	$-\overset{\displaystyle H}{\underset{\displaystyle Cl}{C}}-\overset{\displaystyle H}{\underset{\displaystyle H}{C}}-$	poly(chloroethene)

(a) In general there are two types of polymerization: addition and condensation. Classify the above polymers accordingly.   K (1)

(b) (i) What is the structural formula of the polymer called poly(methyl-2-methylpropenoate)?   C (1)

    (ii) What is the name of the polymer formed from $F_2C=CF_2$?   C (1)

    (iii) Draw the structural formula of the monomer used in making poly(chloroethene).   C (1)

(c) Poly(methyl 2-methylpropenoate) undergoes reversible polymerization.

    (i) What do you understand by the term 'reversible polymerization'? K (1)

    (ii) How would you obtain a sample of the monomer from the polymer?   K (2)

(d) Poly(butene) can be made by free radical polymerization. This involves three stages: initiation, propagation, and termination.

   (i) Draw the structural formula of the monomer, but-2-ene.   C (1)

  (ii) What is a 'free radical'?   K (2)

 (iii) How are free radicals obtained?   K (1)

 (iv) By using a benzene radical and monomer units of but-2-ene, show how polymerization takes place through the stages of initiation, propagation, and termination.   H (4)

Total   15 marks

96 Polymers II*

Read the following extract† and then answer the questions.

In 1954 G.Natta and his co-workers in Italy using Ziegler-type catalysts (mixtures of organo-metallic compounds) under closely controlled physical conditions succeeded in obtaining high relative molecular mass polymers from propene (propylene). Previously, the polymers which had been obtained from substituted alkenes had a random arrangement of the polymer units. The latter polymers are known as atactic polymers. In atactic poly(alkene) the alkyl groups are arranged at random relative to each other and the main direction of the polymer chain (a bold line denotes a bond projecting out from the plane of the paper towards the observer whilst a broken line denotes a bond directed into the paper). The poly(propene) obtained by Natta consisted largely of material having an orderly arrangement of the polymer units and is said to be isotactic. In isotactic poly(alkene) the bond to the alkyl groups all project in the same direction.

The structure of an atactic poly(alkene) is given below

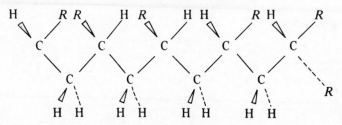

(a) What is an organo-metallic compound? Give an example.   C (2)

(b)   (i)   What is the structural formula of propene?   C (1)

      (ii)   What is the structural formula of a unit of poly(propene)?   C (1)

(c) Where is the propene obtained from in industry?   K (2)

(d) What conditions are necessary in industry to polymerize propene into poly(propene)?   K (2)

(e) Draw the structure of isotactic poly(propene) in a form similar to that shown for an atactic poly(alkene).   H (2)

(f) The use of Ziegler catalysts in polymerization produces polymers which have different properties from polymers made by other methods. Suggest how the properties of Ziegler poly(ethene) differ from high pressure poly(ethene) in terms of

---

†Adapted from J. R. Atkinson, 'Polymer Structures', *Educ. in Chem.*, 1967, **4**, No. 3, 127–134.

(i)	density.	H(1)
(ii)	tensile strength.	H(1)
(iii)	softening point.	H(1)
(iv)	elongation at the breaking point.	H(1)
(v)	crystallinity.	H(1)

Total   15 marks

97 Polymers III*

The following questions are concerned with four polymeric substances.

Polymer type	Formula
Poly(amides)	$-(CH_2)_n-CO-NH-(CH_2)_m-NH-OC-$
Poly(esters)	$-(CH_2)_n-\overset{\displaystyle \|}{\underset{\displaystyle O}{C}}-O-(CH_2)_m-O-\overset{\displaystyle \|}{\underset{\displaystyle O}{C}}-$

Urea-methanal

Phenol-methanal

(a) (i)   What is the general name given to the polymers in the above list? K (1)

(ii) What is the essential difference between the first two and the last two polymers in the list?   C (2)

(b) (i)   What are the structural formulae of ethane-1,2-diol (ethylene glycol) and hexane-1,6-dioic acid (adipic acid)?   C (2)

(ii) What would be the structural formula of the polyester formed between ethane-1,2-diol and hexane-1,6-dioic acid?   H (1)

(iii) How would you attempt to prepare this polyester in the laboratory?   H (2)

(iv) If the ethane-1,2-diol were replaced by propane-1,2,3-triol (glycerol), what change in the polymer structure would you expect?   H (2)

(c) (i)   How can hexanedioic acid be converted into hexanedioyl chloride (adipyl chloride)? Include an equation in your answer.   C (2)

(ii) What is the structural formula of the polymer obtained when hexanedioyl chloride is reacted with hexane-1,6-diamine?   H (1)

114

(iii) What are the values of *m* and *n* in this polymer?   C(1)

(iv) Which link in your formula in (c)(ii) can be compared with that which occurs in the structure of proteins?   C(1)

Total   15 marks

98 Polymer formula*

A sample of a solid organic compound X was analyzed for common elements and was found to contain only carbon and hydrogen.

Relative atomic masses: H = 1, C = 12.

(a) How can the presence of carbon and hydrogen be detected in an organic compound? K (3)

(b) It was found that the percentage of carbon and hydrogen in X were 85·7 and 14·3 per cent respectively. What is the empirical formula of the compound? C (3)

(c) A sample of the compound was completely vaporized and then burnt in oxygen, according to the following equation.

$$C_x H_y\,(g) + (x + y/4)O_2\,(g) \rightarrow xCO_2\,(g) + y/2H_2O\,(g)$$

When 1 cm^3 of the vapour was burnt with an excess volume of oxygen, it was found that the volume of carbon dioxide produced was 15 000 cm^3 and the volume of oxygen used was 22 250 cm^3.

(i) What is the value of x? C (2)

(ii) What is the value of y? C (2)

(d) (i) What type of hydrocarbon does your answer in (c) suggest? H (1)

(ii) Suggest a structure for the hydrocarbon which adequately represents your findings in (b) and (c). H (2)

(e) Comment on the statement that X does not have a single value of relative molecular mass. H (2)

Total 15 marks

99 Infra red spectroscopy*

Read the following carefully and then answer the questions.

The fundamental equation in spectroscopy is $E = h\nu$, where h is Planck's constant (its value is $6 \cdot 6 \times 10^{-34}$ J s) and ν is the frequency of radiation and is related to the wavelength, λ, by $\nu = c/\lambda$. The equation is concerned with the absorption or emission of energy in the form of electromagnetic radiation by an atom or molecule.

Organic chemistry is often concerned with structure determination and here spectroscopy is a valuable tool. The most commonly used part of the electromagnetic spectrum is the infra red region. Every organic bond has its own characteristic frequency at which infra red radiation is absorbed. The radiation is absorbed because of some change, such as stretching, which occurs in the molecule. Thus by studying the energies of absorptions the structure of molecules may be determined.

Velocity of electromagnetic radiation in vacuo $= c = 3 \times 10^8$ m s^{-1}

(a) The wavelength of typical infra red radiation is 10^4 nm.

    (i) What is the frequency of this radiation?   C(1)

    (ii) What is the energy of a quantum of radiation at this frequency? H(1)

(b) Energy is absorbed because a bond is stretched.

    (i) Show diagrammatically how a C—H bond could be stretched.   C(1)

    (ii) Suggest another mechanism by which radiation would be absorbed.   C(1)

(c)   (i) What is the structural formula of hex-1-ene?   C(1)

    (ii) Draw the two possible geometrical isomers of hex-2-ene.   H(2)

   (iii) How can infra red spectroscopy be used to distinguish between hex-1-ene and hex-2-ene?   C(3)

(d) The following list gives the position of various infra red absorptions in organic compounds.

Bond		Wavelength μm
C–H stretch	(in –CH=CH$_2$)	3·2
C–H stretch	(in –CH=CH–)	3·3
C–H stretch	(in –CH$_3$, –CH$_2$–)	3·4
C=C stretch	(in –CH=CH– and –CH=CH$_2$)	6·1
C–H bend	(in –CH$_2$=CH$_2$)	6·8–7·2
C–H bend	(in –CH–CH$_2$)	9·9, 10·9
C–H bend	(in –(CH$_2$)$_3$–)	13·5
C–H bend	(in –CH=CH-(*trans*))	10·2
C–H bend	(in –CH=CH-(*cis*))	14·3

(i) In a sample of hexene the following positions of absorptions were noted: 3·5, 3·4, 6·1, 6·8-7·2, and 10·2 μm. What is the structure of the sample of hexene? Give your reasons. H(3)

(ii) How could this structure be confirmed using ozonolysis? H(2)

Total   15 marks

100 Organic mass spectrometry*

When a hydrocarbon of molecular formula C_6H_{12} was introduced into a low resolution mass spectrometer (i.e. only singly charged ions produced) the following was recorded.

Relative atomic masses: H = 1, C = 12

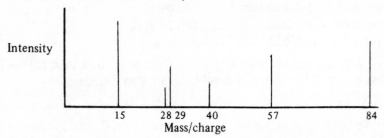

Mass/charge

It was also found that the hydrocarbon decolorized bromine water and on ozonolysis followed by water yielded an aldehyde and a ketone.

(a) How can the mass spectrometer help to elucidate the structure of an organic substance?   K (2)

(b) Where would the following ions appear on the mass spectrum: CH_3^+, $C_2H_5^+$, and CH_3CH^+?   H (3)

(c) What can be deduced from the fact that the hydrocarbon decolorizes bromine water and reacts with trioxygen (ozone)?   C (1)

(d) The aldehyde and ketone produced from ozonolysis were ethanal (acetaldehyde) and butanone (ethyl methyl ketone) respectively.

   (i) Draw the structural formula of butanone.   C (1)

   (ii) Describe one chemical test that you could perform in order to distinguish between ethanal and butanone.   H (2)

(e) (i) Suggest a structure for the hydrocarbon.   H (1)

   (ii) Name this structure.   C (1)

   (iii) Can any geometrical isomers exist for the compound in (e)(i)? Give your reasons.   H (2)

(f) On the basis of your answer in (e)(i) suggest possible ions to account for the peaks on the mass spectrum at 28 and 40.   H (2)

Total   15 marks

Answers to some numerical questions

1 (a) (i) 248   (ii) 0·1   (iii) 0·08   (iv) 0·004
   (b) (i) 0·02   (ii) 0·0005
   (c) (i) 0·0025   (ii) 0·0015   (iii) 3

2 (a) (i) 40   (ii) 1 mol dm^{-3} (iii) 0·4
   (b) (i) 0·35   (ii) 0·05   (iii) 2·5 × 10^{-3}
   (c) (ii) 5:2   (iii) 0·35

3 (a) (i) 640   (ii) 192 300   (iii) 2   (iv) 2L (vi) 6·01 × 10^{23} mol^{-1}
   (b) (i) 6·39 × 10^{15} (ii) 1·03 × 10^{-8} (iii) 6·20 × 10^{23} mol^{-1}

4 (f) (iii) 85·56

5 (a) (ii) 0·0042   (iii) 63·57   (iv) 23·8 dm^3

6 (a) (ii) 1450 s
   (b) (ii) 4·7 × 10^{-4} s^{-1}

13 (b) (iii) 143 pm

14 (a) (i) 17·46 cm^3 (ii) 18 cm^3 (iv) 3

15 (b) (ii) 218 K

17 (c) (ii) −2513 kJ mol^{-1}
   (d) (i) 4500 kJ mol

18 (d) (i) −753 kJ mol^{-1}

21 (c) (i) 0.04 mol dm^{-3}

22 (a) (ii) 4·77:
   (b) (ii) ≏ 2·24 × 10^{-2} mol dm^{-3} (c) (iv) ≏ 1·65
   (c) (i) 8·7 × 10^{-12} mol dm^{-3} (c) (iii) 1·14 cm^3

23 (c) (ii) 4·58

25 (b) (ii) 8 × 10^{-2} mol^{-2} m^{-6} s^{-1}
   (c) (i) 5·12 mol m^{-3} s^{-1}

27 (b) (iii) 1 10 kJ mol^{-1} (iv) ≏ 10^{21}

28 (b) (ii) 0·62 V   (iv) 120 kJ mol^{-1}

29 (b) 1·43

30 (a) (i) 0·5 cm^{-1} (ii) 1·2 × 10^{20}

38 (b) −532 kJ mol^{-1}

41 (g) (ii) 2×10^{-3} (iii) 2×10^{-3} (iv) $12 \cdot 5 \times 10^{-3}$ (v) $208 + 18x$
(vi) 2

43 (e) 212 kg

44 (c) (i) $7 \cdot 9 \times 10^{-7}$ mol dm^{-3} (ii) $8 \cdot 2$

47 (a) (i) $133 \cdot 4$ (ii) 267

53 (g) (iii) $\simeq 3 \cdot 2$

55 (d) $15 \cdot 5$ g

57 (d) -340 kJ mol^{-1} (e) $-0 \cdot 13$ V

68 (e) 43 kJ mol^{-1}

69 (a) (ii) $6 \cdot 7$, $3 \cdot 3$

70 (f) (i) $0 \cdot 0009$ (ii) $0 \cdot 036$

74 (a) (i) $0 \cdot 01$ (ii) $0 \cdot 03$ (iv) 1080 cm^3 (v) $0 \cdot 54$ g

77 (e) (i) $0 \cdot 72$ g   (ii) $0 \cdot 0051$ (iii) $0 \cdot 0051$ (iv) 123 cm^3 (v) 20

80 (a) (ii) 3316 kJ mol^{-1} (iii) 650 kJ mol^{-1} (iv) 325 kJ mol^{-1}

83 (l) (iii) $0 \cdot 005$ (iv) $0 \cdot 005$ (v) $0 \cdot 98$ g

85 (c) 90 kJ mol^{-1}

89 (a) (ii) $9 \cdot 4$

94 (e) (ii) 7   (iii) 5, 4

99 (a) (i) 3×10^{13} Hz   (ii) $19 \cdot 8 \times 10^{-21}$ J

ISBN 0 340 20831 7

First printed 1977
Reprinted 1978, with revisions 1980, 1981

Typesetting by Tecmedia
Printed in Great Britain for
Hodder and Stoughton Educational
a division of Hodder and Stoughton Ltd,
Mill Road, Dunton Green, Sevenoaks, Kent,
by Whitstable Litho Ltd.,
Whitstable, Kent